Earth Science 6
Learning Coach Guide

Part 1

D1264957

About K12 Inc.

K12 Inc., a technology-based education company, is the nation's leading provider of proprietary curriculum and online education programs to students in grades K–12. K¹² provides its curriculum and academic services to online schools, traditional classrooms, blended school programs, and directly to families. K12 Inc. also operates the K¹² International Academy, an accredited, diploma-granting online private school serving students worldwide. K¹²'s mission is to provide any child the curriculum and tools to maximize success in life, regardless of geographic, financial, or demographic circumstances. K12 Inc. is accredited by CITA. More information can be found at www.K12.com.

978-1-60153-346-3

Printed by Courier, Kendallville, IN, USA, April 2014, Lot 042014

Table of Contents

Learning Coach Guide
Lesson 1: Introduction to Earth Science

This is an introductory lesson in which your student will learn about the topics he will explore in the Earth Science course. Your student will read an overview of the units of study that compose the course and prepare a Science Notebook.

Lesson Objectives
- Explore concepts to be addressed during the year in Earth Science.

PREPARE

Approximate lesson time is 60 minutes.

Materials
For the Student

      Keeping a Science Notebook

        binder, 3-ring

        folders

        hole punch

        tabbed dividers

        paper

TEACH
Activity 1: Welcome to Earth Science *(Online)*
Instructions
Your student will read an overview of the topics addressed in this portion of Earth Science.

Activity 2: Keeping a Science Notebook *(Offline)*
Instructions
Your student will learn how to set up and organize a Science Notebook. He may need your help in finding materials, writing on tabbed dividers, and putting together the notebook.

Learning Coach Guide
Lesson 2: Spheres of the Earth

Your student will learn about the components of different spheres of the earth: atmosphere, biosphere, lithosphere, hydrosphere, and magnetosphere.

Lesson Objectives

- Describe features of the layers, or spheres, that make up the earth system (atmosphere, biosphere, lithosphere, hydrosphere, and magnetosphere).
- Explain that the earth is made up of layers (internally and on the surface).
- Define the biosphere as the zone of life on Earth that includes all living things.

PREPARE

Approximate lesson time is 60 minutes.

Materials

For the Student

- Which Sphere?
- Spheres of the Earth Lesson Review

For the Adult

- Which Sphere? Answer Key
- Spheres of the Earth Lesson Review Answer Key

Keywords and Pronunciation

atmosphere : the gaseous layer surrounding the earth, made up of the mixture of substances known as air; the earth's atmosphere is made up of many gases, including the oxygen we need to breathe, as well as small liquid and solid particles

aurora : streamers or bands of light sometimes visible in the night sky in northern or southern regions of the earth; scientists think an aurora is caused by charged particles from the sun that enter the earth's magnetic field and stimulate molecules in the atmosphere

biosphere (BIY-uh-sfir) : the zone of life on the earth that includes all living things; plants, fungi, and animals are all parts of the earth's biosphere

hydrosphere (HIY-druh-sfir) : the liquid layer of the earth, made up of the earth's waters; the oceanic parts of the hydrosphere cover about three-fourths of the earth's surface

lithosphere (LIH-the-sfir) : the rocky outer layer of the solid earth, averaging about 100 km in depth; the lithosphere includes the continents, islands, and the entire ocean floor

magnetosphere (mag-NEE-tuh-sfir) : the region in space that is affected by the earth's magnetic field; solar wind and other particles in space are deflected by the earth's magnetosphere

TEACH
Activity 1: More than Meets the Eye *(Online)*
Instructions
In this activity, your student will read about the parts of the earth known as spheres, such as the atmosphere and hydrosphere. Your student will discover how these spheres interact with one another and support life on earth.

Activity 2: Which Sphere? *(Offline)*
Instructions
Your student will read about common events and identify which of earth's five spheres covered in the lesson are involved in each. He will then write original events involving one or more of earth's spheres. Refer your student to the Explore section of the lesson for descriptions of each sphere.

Activity 3: Spheres of the Earth *(Offline)*
Instructions
In this activity, your student will review the concepts learned in this lesson. Store the review sheet in your student's Science Notebook.

ASSESS

Lesson Assessment: Spheres of the Earth (*Online*)
Students will complete an online assessment based on the lesson objectives. The assessment will be scored by the computer. The attached answer key is the most current and may not coincide with previously printed guides.

Name _____   Date _____

Which Sphere? Answer Key

Anything that happens on earth occurs within one or more of earth's spheres. Below you will find several statements describing events that take place every day.

Identify which sphere(s) are involved in each event. Label each statement with a **H, B, A, L**, and/or **M** indicating that it takes place in either the *hydrosphere, biosphere, atmosphere, lithosphere, or magnetosphere*. You may use some letters more than once, and some statements may describe events that occur in more than one sphere simultaneously.

B   1. Bees pollinating flowers.

L,A   2. Desert sand blowing across the dunes.

L,B   3. A farmer plowing the earth to plant crops.

A   4. Clouds floating in the sky.

H   5. Water flowing in a river.

H,B   6. Fish swimming in the ocean.

M   7. The Earth being protected from charged particles.

L,H   8. Snow on the Rocky Mountains.

A   9. A foggy day.

L,H   10. Waves pounding and shaping cliffs.

Describe the Sphere

Now it is your turn to observe the world around you and describe the ways in which the spheres of the earth work together to shape our beautiful planet. Create a one-sentence statement to illustrate the interaction of the following spheres.

Answers will vary.

11. The lithosphere and the biosphere

   Building a house on a hill

12. The atmosphere and the hydrosphere

   The water cycle

13. The biosphere and the hydrosphere

   Crayfish swimming in a creek

14. The atmosphere and the biosphere

   Birds flying in the sky

15. The lithosphere, hydrosphere, and biosphere

   Offshore oil drilling

16. The atmosphere, lithosphere, and hydrosphere

   Wind and water erosion of the Grand Canyon

Name _____   Date _____

Spheres of the Earth Lesson Review Answer Key

Review what you have learned about earth's spheres. When finished, place your completed lesson review sheet in your Science Notebook.

Making an Outline

Taking notes in an outline helps you organize information that has many parts. Broad subjects make up the major headings, and details are underneath. Roman numerals and letters are used to organize them.

Read the Explore section of your lesson and fill in the blanks in the outline below.

Earth's Spheres

1. **Biosphere**

    a. contains all life on earth

    b. examples: plants, animals, fungi

2. **Hydrosphere**

    a. contains all water on earth

    b. examples: oceans, lakes, rivers

3. **Lithosphere**

    a. rocky outer layer of solid earth

    b. examples: mountains, plains, ocean floor

4. **Atmosphere**

    a. contains: air, water gas

    b. examples:clouds, oxygen, carbon dioxide

5. **Magnetosphere**

    a. Contains: magnetic field around earth

    b. example: auroras, where charged particles are trapped

Learning Coach Guide
Lesson 3: Mapping the Earth

We can use maps to name any spot on earth. Maps allow us to communicate about where an earthquake happens, where a tornado is and where it is heading, or to locate the very spot on earth upon which we are standing. But maps can be tricky, too. They are a two-dimensional representation of a three-dimensional object. Your student will learn about maps and how they can be an outstanding earth science tool.

Lesson Objectives

- Interpret maps using scale, directional indicators, keys, and symbols to locate physical features.
- Use latitude and longitude to locate places on a map.
- Determine the scale of a map.

PREPARE

Approximate lesson time is 60 minutes.

Advance Preparation

- If you don't already have it, you will need to gather dried beans or peas.

Materials

For the Student

    📖 Ring of Fire

    beans, dry - (or dried peas)

    K12 Wall Map

    📖 Mapping the Earth Lesson Review

For the Adult

    📖 Ring of Fire Answer Key

    📖 Mapping the Earth Lesson Review Answer Key

Keywords and Pronunciation

cartographer (kahr-TAH-gruh-fuhr) : a person who makes maps

latitude (LA-tuh-tood) : a distance in degrees north and south of the equator

longitude (LAHN-juh-tood) : a particular distance east or west of the prime meridian running through Greenwich, England, measured as an angle at the earth´s center and expressed in degrees; lines of longitude meet at the poles

map legend : a section of a map that explains the meanings of symbols and that may contain the map scale; symbols for airports, recreation areas, campsites, and other areas of interest may appear in a map legend

map projection : a way to transfer information from a three-dimensional curved surface to a two-dimensional medium, such as paper or a computer screen

meridians : lines of longitude that run vertically from the north pole to the south pole; meridians terminate at the poles

prime meridian (priym muh-RIH-dee-uhn) : the imaginary vertical line, running north to south, from which longitude is measured; the prime meridian runs right through England

---

TEACH
Activity 1: Round Earth, Flat Map *(Online)*
Instructions
Your student will be introduced to several different types of maps and will explore some of the limitations of using a flat map to represent the three-dimensional world.

Activity 2: Ring of Fire *(Online)*
Instructions
Your student will practice using latitude and longitude to plot locations of volcanoes in the Ring of Fire.

Activity 3: Mapping the Earth *(Offline)*
Instructions
In this activity, your student will review the concepts learned in this lesson. Store the review sheet in your student's Science Notebook.

ASSESS
Lesson Assessment: Mapping the Earth (*Offline*)
Students will complete an offline assessment based on the lesson objectives. Print the assessment and have students complete it on their own. Use the answer key to score the assessment, and then enter the results online. The attached answer key is the most current and may not coincide with previously printed guides.

Name _____ Date _____

Ring of Fire Answer Key

The Ring of Fire sounds much like what it describes—a region of mountain building, earthquakes, and volcanoes surrounding the Pacific Ocean. Use latitude and longitude to map the Ring of Fire by locating the volcanoes in the table below and on the next page.

Spread your wall map of the world out on the floor. Use dried beans or dried peas to plot the locations of the volcanoes on your map.

	Location	Check When Plotted
Rincon de la Vieja, Costa Rica	10° N, 85° W	✓
Cerro Negro, Nicaragua	12° N, 86° W	✓
Pacaya, Guatemala	14° N, 90° W	✓
Popocatepetl, Mexico	19° N, 99° W	✓
Mount Saint Helens, Washington	46° N, 122° W	✓
Amukta, Alaska	52° N, 171° W	✓
Kliuchevskoi, Russia	56° N, 160° E	✓
Ruapehu, New Zealand	39° S, 175° E	✓
Metis Shoal, Tonga Islands	19° S, 174° W	✓
Kilauea, Hawaii	19° N, 155° W	✓
Canlaon, Philippines	10° N, 123° E	✓
Papandayan, Java, Indonesia	7° S, 108° E	✓
Soufriere Hills, Montserrat, West Indies	16° N, 62° W	✓
Mayon, Philippines	13° N, 123° E	✓
San Cristobal, Nicaragua	12° N, 87° W	✓
Mount Lewotobi, Indonesia	8° S, 122° E	✓
Asama, Honshu, Japan	36° N, 138° E	✓

The Ring of Fire

	Location	Check When Plotted
Krakatau, Indonesia	6° S, 105° E	✓
Colima, Mexico	19° N, 103° W	✓
South Sister, Oregon	44° N, 121° W	✓
Maroa, New Zealand	38° S, 176° E	✓
Rotorua, New Zealand	38° S, 176° E	✓
Taal, Philippines	14° N, 120° E	✓
Shishaldin, Alaska	54° N, 163° W	✓
Korovin, Alaska	52° N, 174° W	✓
Yellowstone, Wyoming	44° N, 110° W	✓
Chiginagak, Alaska	57° N, 157° W	✓
Adatara, Honshu, Japan	37° N, 140° E	✓
Loihi Seamount, Hawaii	18° N, 155° W	✓
Long Valley Caldera, California	37° N, 118° W	✓
Akutan, Alaska	54° N, 166° W	✓
Hosho, Kyushu, Japan	33° N, 131° E	✓

What patterns do you see in the points that you plotted?

You should notice that the points you plotted form a ring shape.

Name _____   Date _____

Mapping the Earth Lesson Review Answer Key

1. latitude, north, south

2. meridians

3. longitude, east, west

4. farther apart, closer together

5. equator, prime meridian

6. about 20 km (12.5 mi)

7. about 28 km (17 mi)

8. latitude should be given first, followed by longitude

Name _____   Date _____

Mapping the Earth Lesson Assessment Answer Key

Map Essentials

1. 10° S, 35° E

2. 15° S, 46° E

3. 15° S, 50° E

4. five

5. SE

6. three

7. approximately 60 km

8. Surfer's Town

Learning Coach Guide
Lesson 4: Mapping Earth's Physical Features

Geologists often use topographic maps when they're doing research. A topographic map gives data on the rise and fall of the land. Modern computer techniques, such as geographic information system (GIS) technology and photogrammetry, have increased the accuracy of maps and their usefulness. Your student will learn how to interpret data on a topographic map in this lesson.

Lesson Objectives

- Analyze topographic maps.
- Define topography as the physical features of an area of land, including mountains, valleys, plains, and bodies of water.
- Identify a topographic map as a representation of the earth's surface.

PREPARE

Approximate lesson time is 60 minutes.

Materials

For the Student

    📇 Topo Challenge Map Key

    📇 Lesson Review

For the Adult

    📇 Lesson Review Answer Key

Keywords and Pronunciation

cartographer (kahr-TAH-gruh-fuhr) : a person who makes maps

contour interval : the difference in elevation between contour lines;a contour interval of 10 meters indicates that the contour lines on the map show 10-meter differences in elevation

contour line : on a map, the line connecting points having the same elevations above sea level;contour lines that are spaced close together on a map show an area with a steep slope

elevation : distance of something above a reference point (such as sea level)

topographic (tah-puh-GRA-fihk)

topographic map (tah-puh-GRA-fihk) : a map showing elevation of land in relation to sea level; a topographic map may use contour lines to show elevation

topography (tuh-PAH-gruh-fee) : physical features of an area of land

---

TEACH
Activity 1: The Lay of the Land *(Online)*

Instructions

Your student will study the usefulness of topographic maps and their symbols.

Activity 2: Topo Challenge *(Online)*

Instructions

Your student will practice reading a variety of topographic maps of increasing difficulty. He will analyze each map and locate features using a map key. Several topographic maps are available online for free. Look for maps or aerial photographcs of your area online.

Activity 3: Mapping Earth's Physical Features *(Offline)*

Instructions

In this activity, your student will review the concepts learned in this lesson. Store the review sheet in your student's Science Notebook.

ASSESS

Lesson Assessment: Mapping Earth's Physical Features (*Online*)

Students will complete an online assessment based on the lesson objectives. The assessment will be scored by the computer. The attached answer key is the most current and may not coincide with previously printed guides.

Name _____   Date _____

Mapping Earth's Physical Features Lesson Review Answer Key

Vocabulary Review

Topographic Maps

A topographic map is designed to show the rise and fall of the landscape. Contour lines show how far the land rises above sea level, or its elevation. The distance between two contour lines is known as the contour interval. A cartographer carefully constructs topographic maps using information, photographs, and technology.

Map Skills

1. 5 meters

2. east

3. east

4. seven

Learning Coach Guide
Lesson 5: Weathering

Your student will study how mechanical and chemical weathering breaks down rock and reshapes the surface of the earth. He will observe examples of weathering either outside or online and then describe his observations with pictures and descriptions.

Lesson Objectives

- Explain that weathering produces sediments that contribute to soil formation (sand, silt, clay).
- Give examples of how climate differences influence the rate of weathering.
- Define weathering.

PREPARE

Approximate lesson time is 60 minutes.

Materials

For the Student

📖 Weathering in Action Activity Sheet

📖 Weathering Lesson Review

For the Adult

📖 Weathering Lesson Review Answer Key

Keywords and Pronunciation

chemical weathering : the breaking up of rocks by chemical reactions; natural acids dissolved in rainwater are important agents of chemical weathering of rocks

ice wedging : a type of mechanical weathering in which water seeps into the cracks in a rock, freezes and expands, and splits the rock apart

lichen (LIY-kuhn) : a life form which grows as crusty patches on soil, rocks, and trees; lichen forms when an alga and a fungus grow together

mechanical weathering : the breaking up of rocks by physical forces; mechanical weathering occurs when water expands as it freezes in the crack of a rock, expanding the crack and breaking the rock apart

weathering : the breakdown of rocks by physical or chemical processes; weathering causes the rocks on a cliff to wear away

TEACH
Activity 1: Earth Wears Down (Online)

Activity 2: Weathering in Action (Offline)

Activity 3: Weathering *(Offline)*
Instructions
In this activity, your student will review the concepts learned in this lesson. Store the review sheet in your student's Science Notebook.

ASSESS

Lesson Assessment: Weathering, Part 1 (*Online*)
Students will complete an online assessment based on the lesson objectives. The assessment will be scored by the computer. The attached answer key is the most current and may not coincide with previously printed guides.

Lesson Assessment: Weathering, Part 2 (*Offline*)
Students will complete an offline assessment based on the lesson objectives. Print the assessment and have students complete it on their own. Use the answer key to score the assessment, and then enter the results online. The attached answer key is the most current and may not coincide with previously printed guides.

Name _____   Date _____

Weathering Lesson Review Answer Key

Review what you have learned about weathering. When finished, place your completed lesson review sheet in your Science Notebook.

Making a Venn Diagram

A Venn diagram is a special tool to help you compare different ideas that have some things in common. Use the words or phrases from the Word Bank to fill in the Venn diagram below. Put words or phrases relating to chemical weathering in the right circle and words or phrases having to do with mechanical weathering in the left circle. Words or phrases relating to both mechanical and chemical weathering should be placed in the area marked "Both."

Word Bank

breaks down rocks into small pieces	can be caused by acids in rain water	plant roots
causes physical changes	changes the earth's landscape	ice wedging
causes chemical changes in rocks	can cause rust on some rocks	
small pieces of sand, silt, and clay become soil		

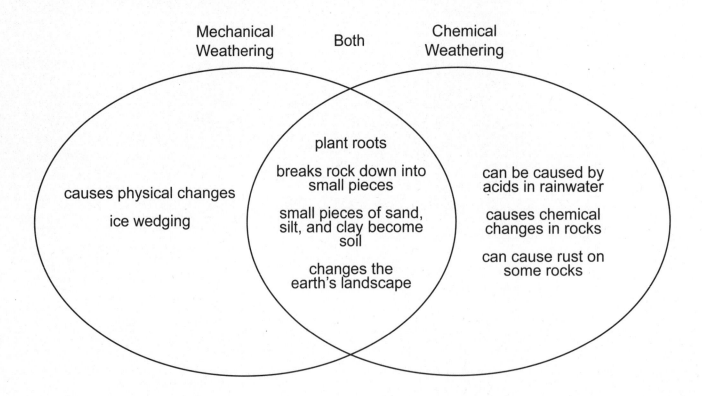

Mechanical Weathering
- causes physical changes
- ice wedging

Both
- plant roots
- breaks rock down into small pieces
- small pieces of sand, silt, and clay become soil
- changes the earth's landscape

Chemical Weathering
- can be caused by acids in rainwater
- causes chemical changes in rocks
- can cause rust on some rocks

Name _____   Date _____

Weathering, Part 2 Lesson Assessment Answer Key

1. Answers may vary but should include the following: Solid rock wears down into smaller pieces when mechanical and chemical weathering occurs. These pieces of rock (clay, silt, sand) mix with water, air, and other matter. Over time, soil is created.

2. Answers may vary but should include the following: Water carries chemicals that can wear away rocks, so chemical weathering happens faster in areas with more moisture and humidity. Areas with wet climates have more plants and microorganisms than drier areas, and these plants and microorganisms produce chemicals that can cause weathering; plant activity can also lead to mechanical weathering. The conditions in tropical rain forests offer just the right combination of things for weathering to occur.

Learning Coach Guide
Lesson 6: Erosion

Water, wind, and ice can mold and reshape earth's surface. As rain falls, water is absorbed into the soil and travels through many layers of rock. Or it can move along the ground, joining rivers and carving into the landscape. In some cases, it can even help shape amazing caves.

Lesson Objectives
- Describe major causes, processes, and consequences of erosion.
- Define erosion.
- Identify surface structures that show the effects of erosion.

PREPARE

Approximate lesson time is 60 minutes.

Advance Preparation
- You will need to go outside to complete this activity. If you are not able to go outside, complete the activity inside using a large plastic tub.
- You will need to save some sand for the Lab:Desertification lesson.

Materials
For the Student
> books
> household item
> sand
> baking dish
> measuring cup
> water
> 🖳 Erosion Lesson Review

For the Adult
> 🖳 Erosion Lesson Review Answer Key

Keywords and Pronunciation
agent : a force or material that causes a change
deposition : the process in which rock and soil particles move from water, wind, or ice onto the land
erosion : the gradual removal of the surface of the land by water, wind, or glaciers
glacier (GLAY-shur) : large moving masses of ice and snow on land
mass wasting : the downhill movement of rock and soil; also known as mass movement
meander (mee-AN-duhr) : a turn or winding of a stream or river; as a river ages, reaching a flat area, it tends to form meanders as it flows back and forth across the landscape
rivulet (RIH-vyuh-luht) : a small stream; a rivulet often flows into a larger stream

TEACH
Activity 1: Erosion *(Online)*
Instructions
Your student will learn that water, ice, and wind remove, transport, and deposit rock debris in the process of erosion. Gravity is part of the process, too. Water is the most common and powerful agent of erosion.

Activity 2: Fast-Forward Erosion *(Offline)*
Instructions
Your student will recreate conditions of erosion using common materials and analyze the "landforms" that occur as a result.

Tip
It is very important for your student to add the water slowly to get useful results. If you are unable to complete the activity outside, you can try it in your kitchen sink or in a large tub.

Answers
1. The sand erodes where the water falls from the faucet onto the sand. It also erodes where the resulting stream flows downhill. The water flows quickly over areas where sand is eroded.
2. The sand is transported down the "rivers." It is deposited at the bottom of the "rivers."
3. The water flowing down the slope makes channels that are V-shaped.
4. The delta forms in a triangular or fanlike shape.

Science Club Idea
This activity can easily be done by student partners or groups. Watch the effects of erosion during the activity, and then plan an outing with other students to look for examples of erosion in your area. Examples can be seen in parks or wooded areas, along streams and creeks, and among sand dunes.

Activity 3: Erosion *(Offline)*
Instructions
In this activity, your student will review the concepts learned in this lesson. Store the review sheet in your student's Science Notebook.

ASSESS

Lesson Assessment: Erosion, Part 1 *(Online)*
Students will complete an online assessment based on the lesson objectives. The assessment will be scored by the computer. The attached answer key is the most current and may not coincide with previously printed guides.

Lesson Assessment: Erosion, Part 2 *(Offline)*
Students will complete an offline assessment based on the lesson objectives. Print the assessment and have students complete it on their own. Use the answer key to score the assessment, and then enter the results online. The attached answer key is the most current and may not coincide with previously printed guides.

Name _____ Date _____

Erosion Lesson Review Answer Key

Review what you have learned about erosion. When finished, place your completed lesson review sheet in your Science Notebook.

Erosion Notes

Using tables to take notes can help organize details of new information. Find the information from the lesson to fill in the table below.

Cause of erosion	Example(s) of where it occurs	Example(s) of feature(s) it forms
liquid water	rivers, beaches, streams, rivulets	meanders, cliffs, valleys, canyons
wind	deserts	unusually shaped rocks
glaciers or ice	areas near the poles or mountaintops	U-shaped valleys

1. Erosion and weathering are often confused. How is erosion different from weathering? _____
Weathering is the process in which rock is broken down into smaller pieces. Erosion is the process in which rock and soil pieces are moved over the land by water, wind, ice, or other mechanisms.

Name _____   Date _____

Erosion, Part 2 Lesson Assessment Answer Key

1. Answer should include: Like a bulldozer, a glacier pushes soil and rocks of all sizes as it gradually moves. As a glacier moves, it carves out valleys and deposits material along the way.

2. Drawing should show how moving water picks up soil particles and breaks up rock, transporting these materials and depositing them in different places. The drawing might also show how water carves out canyons and how meandering rivers bend and twist as they reshape the land. Examples of possible drawings can be found at http://home. mindspring.com/~cms-stuff/id6.html, http://eunicea.glogster.com/geography/, and http://www. geographylwc.org.uk/GCSE/igcse/rivergcase/landmid.html.

Learning Coach Guide
Lesson 7: Soils of the Earth

All soil has its beginnings in rocks. Depending on the climate and the original type of rock, different types of soils can form. Your student will study the processes that form soils, as well as the characteristics of three types of soils: sand, silt, and clay.

Lesson Objectives

- Explain how soil is formed.
- Describe the three major soil types: sand, silt, and clay.
- Relate soil types to climate.

PREPARE

Approximate lesson time is 60 minutes.

Materials

For the Student

    📄 Graph Paper

    📄 Working with Scientific Data

       pencils, colored 12

    📄 Soils of the Earth Lesson Review

For the Adult

    📄 Working With Scientific Data Answer Key

    📄 Soils of the Earth Lesson Review Answer Key

Keywords and Pronunciation

biome (BIY-ohm) : a large area dominated by characteristic plants and animals, such as a rain forest, desert, or tundra

chemical weathering : the breaking up of rocks by chemical reactions; natural acids dissolved in rainwater are important agents of chemical weathering of rocks

lichen (LIY-kuhn) : a life form which grows as crusty patches on soil, rocks, and trees; lichen forms when an alga and a fungus grow together

loam : a type of soil that has equal parts of sand, silt, and clay; many plants grow well in loam

permeability (puhr-mee-uh-BIH-luh-tee) : the rate at which water passes through a material

porosity (puh-RAH-suh-tee) : the measure of the space between particles in rock or soil; the porosity of soil allows it to soak up rainwater

TEACH
Activity 1: Soils of the Earth *(Online)*

Activity 2: Working with Scientific Data *(Online)*
Instructions
Your student will work with scientific data to analyze the relationship between air temperature and soil temperature. The following suggestions may help your student complete this activity.

- Have your student convert Celsius to Fahrenheit using the Tips.
- For Question 4, have your student use a pencil to draw a line from the horizontal axis of the graph to the air temperature at 12 p.m. Then find the time when the soil temperature rose to the same degree.
- For Question 6, have your student use a pencil and draw a line from the vertical axis of the graph to the high and low temperatures for soil and air.

Activity 3: Soils of the Earth *(Online)*

ASSESS

Lesson Assessment: Soils of the Earth, Part 1 (*Online*)
Students will complete an online assessment based on the lesson objectives. The assessment will be scored by the computer. The attached answer key is the most current and may not coincide with previously printed guides.

Lesson Assessment: Soils of the Earth, Part 2 (*Offline*)
Students will complete an offline assessment based on the lesson objectives. Print the assessment and have students complete it on their own. Use the answer key to score the assessment, and then enter the results online. The attached answer key is the most current and may not coincide with previously printed guides.

Name _____   Date _____

Working With Scientific Data Answer Key

Check your student's graph for accuracy.

1. When air temperature increased, soil temperature increased. When air temperature decreased, soil temperature decreased.

2. Both air temperature and soil temperature would decrease in temperature.

3. Air heats up more quickly than soil. Warm air heats up soil, but soil heats much more slowly than air.

Conclusion

Air heats and cools faster than soil. Keeping track of the weather patterns and air temperature can help farmers prepare for changes in soil temperature. They may want to use surface cover to keep soil cool, or add water to allow heat to flow through soil. Mulch can be used to keep soil warm in the winter and cool in the summer.

Name _____   Date _____

Soils of the Earth Lesson Review Answer Key

1. Sample 1
2. Sample 2
3. Sample 3
4. Sample 1
5. Sample 2
6. Sample 3

Name _____   Date _____

Soils of the Earth, Part 2 Lesson Assessment Answer Key

Read the questions, then answer them in the space provided.

(10 pts.)

1. Describe some actions that may play a role in the process of soil formation.

    Answers will vary but should include: Organisms such as moss or lichen may begin growing

    on rock surfaces. Acids in the plant roots weather the rock surfaces. Weathered pieces of

    rock combine with decaying plants and animals to form soil.

    _____

    _____

    _____

(10 pts.)

2. Name a biome that is likely to have fertile soil and explain why.

    Answers will vary. Sample answer: Grasslands and temperate forests have fertile soil. These

    areas have moderate rainfall, and their soil contains plenty of organic matter, which makes

    them nutrient-rich. The moderate temperatures make it possible for a variety of life to exist in

    these biomes. The abundant presence of living things contributes to the organic matter that

    builds up in soil.

    _____

    _____

Learning Coach Guide
Lesson 8: Soil Profiles

Lesson Objectives

- Investigate and identify the composition of different soils.
- Describe a soil profile, including soil horizons.
- Explain how plants use various components of soils (organic and inorganic).

PREPARE

Approximate lesson time is 60 minutes.

Materials

For the Student

💻 Soil Profiles Lesson Review

For the Adult

💻 Soil Profiles Lesson Review Answer Key

Keywords and Pronunciation

horizon : a soil layer

humus (HYOO-muhs) : the dark portion of soil created by the decay of plant and animal matter

inorganic : non-living

leaching : the process in which water carries nutrients from one layer of soil to a lower layer of soil

nitrogen : a nutrient critical for plant growth

organic : living or once living

soil profile : cross-section of the soil layers above the bedrock

TEACH
Activity 1: Sink Down in the Soil (Online)

Activity 2: Soil Profiles (Online)
Instructions
In this activity, your student will review the concepts learned in this lesson. Store the review sheet in your student's Science Notebook.

ASSESS

Lesson Assessment: Soil Profiles (Online)
Students will complete an offline assessment based on the lesson objectives. Print the assessment and have students complete it on their own. Use the answer key to score the assessment, and then enter the results online. The attached answer key is the most current and may not coincide with previously printed guides.

Name _____   Date _____

Soil Profiles Lesson Review Answer Key

1. B

2. C

3. A

4. B

5. Bedrock

6. A

7. A

8. C

9. Bedrock

Lesson Assessment Answer Key

Draw a diagram (20 pts.)

1. Draw a soil profle showing A, B, and C horizons. Label each horizon and the bedrock. Write a description of each horizon next to the label.

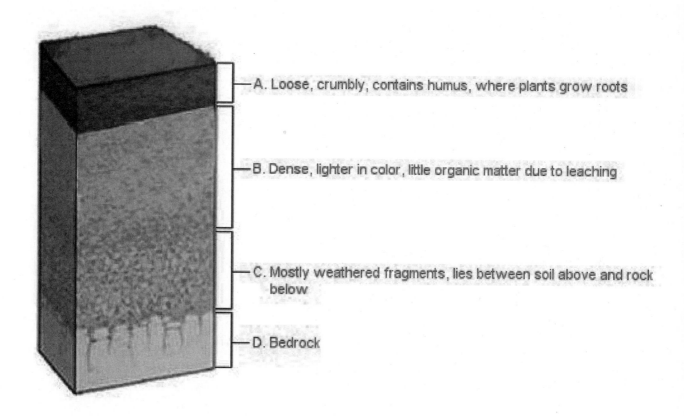

A. Loose, crumbly, contains humus, where plants grow roots

B. Dense, lighter in color, little organic matter due to leaching

C. Mostly weathered fragments, lies between soil above and rock below

D. Bedrock

Short Answer *(6 pts.)*

2. Name some examples of organic and inorganic matter in soils that plants need to grow.

Answers should include: Soil contains organic matter such as decaying plants

and animals and living things such as earthworms, bacteria, and microorganisms.

Inorganic matter in soil includes water, air, and nitrogen.

_____

_____

_____

_____

Learning Coach Guide
Lesson 9: Lab: Desertification

Weathering, erosion, and deposition continually change the shape of our land. In parts of the world where water is scarce and vegetation is thin, the wind is one of the most powerful forces that alters the landscape. Blowing on the desert sand, the wind can shape large hills, known as sand dunes, which sometimes cover fertile fields and even houses.

Your student will learn about a process known as desertification and investigate methods to control the advance of sand into populated areas.

Lesson Objectives

- Record scientific data using charts, graphs, and/or written descriptions.
- Explain how sand dunes are formed and recognize that they have two sides: leeward and windward.
- Conduct an experiment to determine the most effective method for reducing the advancement of sand dunes and deposition of sand in populated areas.
- Record scientific data using charts, graphs, and/or written descriptions.

PREPARE

Approximate lesson time is 60 minutes.

Advance Preparation

- If your sand is moist, open 2 days ahead of time. Put in a shallow pan in a warm place to make sure it's dry. Stir it a couple times a day.

Materials

For the Student

- Graph Paper
- Slowing Down Desertification
  aluminum baking dish - 9 x 13
  modeling clay
  ruler (metric & customary)
  sand, fine
  tub, plastic
  aluminum foil
  coins
  craft sticks
  graduated cylinder
  hair dryer
  oil, cooking

pipe cleaners

safety goggles

scissors

tape - masking

toothpicks

For the Adult

🖳 Lab Answer Key

Keywords and Pronunciation

desertification (dih-ZUHR-tuh-fuh-KAY-shuhn) : loss of productivity of land in relatively dry areas, usually due to human activities that cause damage to the vegetation, but sometimes due to climatic change

drought (drowt) : period of particularly dry weather, bad enough to affect people's lives or the environment

dune : a hill or ridge of wind-blown sand

leeward : on or toward the side to which the wind is blowing

windward : of or on the side exposed to the wind or to prevailing winds

TEACH

Activity 1: Pre-Lab: Erosion and Sand Dunes *(Online)*

Instructions

Your student will briefly review how sand is formed and how sand can prove to be a major problem for desert areas.

Activity 2: Can We Slow the Dunes? *(Offline)*

Instructions

Your student will conduct an experiment to determine the most effective method for reducing sand deposition and dune advancement into populated areas.

Science Club Idea

This is a great activity to do with a partner or in a small group. Plan a science afternoon and get together with other students to complete the lab. Or, suggest to your teacher an online get-together with other students in your school to discuss the different outcomes.

Safety

Electrical appliances must be in good condition. Never allow an electrical appliance to contact water. If one falls into water, do not reach in for it. Turn off power at the panel board or fuse box. Unplug the appliance from the wall by grasping the plug, not the cord. Contact an adult immediately.

When using scissors, knives, or any sharp instrument, always carry them with tips and points facing down and away from you. Cut away from yourself. Never try to catch falling sharp objects. Hold sharp instruments only by the handles. If you cut yourself, notify an adult immediately.

ASSESS

Lesson Assessment: Lab: Desertification (*Offline*)

Review your student's responses on the Slowing Down Desertification lab and input the results online. The attached answer key is the most current and may not coincide with previously printed guides.

Name _____   Date _____

Slowing Down Desertification Answer Key

Sample Data Table

Protection Method	Trial 1 volume of sand (mL)	Trial 2 volume of sand (mL)	Trial 3 volume of sand (mL)	Trial 1 volume of sand (mL)
Control	24	19	23	22
Short Vegetation	9	10	9	9.33
Tall Vegetation	10	12	9	10.33
Straw Grids	20	18	25	21
Sand Fences	5	3	3	3.67
Oil	2	1	2	1.67

Sample Data Graph

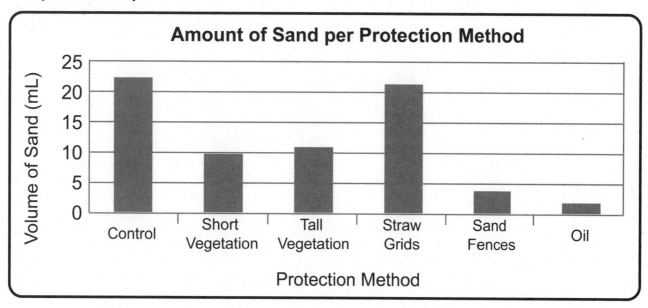

Name _____   Date _____

Student answers will vary but should include the following ideas:

1. The oil was the most effective protection method. It only allowed an average of 1.67 ml of sand to reach the town.

2. Your results are not necessarily the most realistic solution for the problem. Explanations may vary but could include some of the following: In this experiment, the wind was carefully controlled so that it was always blowing in the same direction. In a real-life situation, it is more likely that the wind patterns would vary, at times making certain methods less effective. Additionally, the protection spanned the entire width of the wind. It is highly unlikely that in areas threatened by approaching sand dunes, protection would be able to span the entire width of the dune. It might also be impractical to plant so much vegetation in sandy soil or accumulate enough wood to construct a large sand fence. Materials might not be available in the area for some solutions. Or, the materials might be too expensive. This is an experiment on a small model. Some conditions in a real-life situation could be very different.

3. The least effective method, aside from the no protection, was the straw grids. These allowed nearly the same amount of sand to reach the village as not protection method.

4. It is important in scientific experiments to do several trials. By doing so, you reduce the chance that something unusual will affect your results or that you will just by chance get an unusual result.

5. Testing "no protection" helps determine just how well the protection methods work. It provides a starting point to understand how much effect the protection has on the town. It is also called the "control."

6. These things stayed the same to ensure that the test was done the same way each time. Changing certain measurements could affect the data you collect and you would not be able to make a true comparison among the different methods.

Name _____   Date _____

Lab: Desertification Lesson Assessment Answer Key

Answers:

1. To determine whether or not your student was able to follow the lab procedures in order to successfully conduct the experiment, refer to the **Sample Data Table** in the attached Slowing Down Desertification Lab Answer Key. Answers to the experiment will vary.

2. Refer to the **Sample Data Graph** in the attached Slowing Down Desertification Lab Answer Key to determine if your student was able to successfully create a bar graph based on the data collected in the experiment. Depending on the evidence collected, data entered into the graph will vary.

3. To determine whether your student was able to successfully draw conclusions based on the data gathered during the lab experiment, refer to the **Conclusion** answers on the Slowing Down Desertification Lab Answer Key. Answers to the questions will vary but should include similar ideas to those on the Answer Key.

Learning Coach Guide
Lesson 10. Optional: Your Choice

Lesson Objectives

- Practice skills and reinforce concepts taught in this course.

PREPARE

Approximate lesson time is 60 minutes.

Learning Coach Guide
Lesson 11: Earth's Surface Unit Review

Your student will review his knowledge of the earth's physical systems, mapping techniques, weathering, and soil on an exploration of Antarctica. Then he will experience what a cartographer does as he uses data to map an unmapped island.

Lesson Objectives

- Describe the basic components of the Earth's physical systems: the atmosphere, biosphere, lithosphere, hydrosphere, and magnetosphere.
- Explain latitude and longitude and recognize them as providing a primary coordinate system for reference to places on the earth.
- Describe features on maps such as coordinate systems, scales, directional indicators, keys, symbols, and contour lines.
- Describe specific uses of topographic maps.
- Describe the major processes that break apart and move material around on the earth's surface to form soil from rock and organic material and to change the shape of the surface.
- Describe major agents of mechanical weathering and of chemical weathering, how the agents cause each kind of weathering, and how mechanical weathering and chemical weathering interact to enhance each other's effects.
- Describe major types of soil in terms of porosity, permeability, and climates in which they are found.

PREPARE

Approximate lesson time is 60 minutes.

Materials

For the Student

- 📖 Earth's Surface Unit Review
- 📖 Mapping Mystery Island
- 📖 Mystery Island

For the Adult

- 📖 Unit Review Answer Key
- 📖 Mystery Island Answer Key

TEACH
Activity 1: Where in the World? *(Online)*

Instructions

Your student will review the unit by applying his knowledge of the earth's physical systems, mapping, weathering, and soil to an exercise about Antarctica.

Activity 2: Mapping an Island *(Online)*

Instructions

Even in the twenty-first century, some land remains unexplored. Your student will imagine that he is a cartographer responsible for making an accurate tourist map. He will develop his mapmaking skills by capturing information about the island on a map.

Tips

Your student will have some freedom as to where he places certain features on the map. When you are comparing his map with the answer key, make sure his general locations of features are correct.

Name _____   Date _____

Mapping Mystery Island Answer Key

This is a sample map your student may have produced.

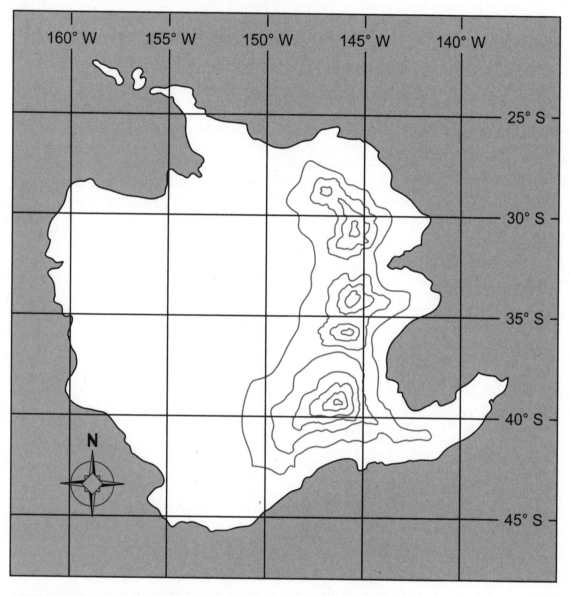

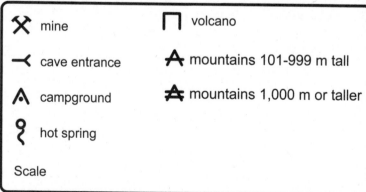

Name _____   Date _____

Earth's Surface Unit Review Answer Key

In this unit, you have learned several things about the earth's surface. As you read about Antarctica, answer the questions below to review what you have learned. You may have to think hard to answer some of them, but you should be able to answer all of them. Refer to the lesson number next to each question if you need more help or you need to review a concept.

Answers may vary but should include the following. Have your student review the lessons in this unit if necessary.

1. How would temperature changes in the atmosphere, enough to melt Antarctic ice, affect the hydrosphere, lithosphere, and biosphere? (Lesson 2)

    The hydrosphere would change as water from the melting ice raised sea levels; coastlines (the lithosphere) would be flooded; living things (biosphere) would have to move if the waters rose.

2. Cold-weather tourists may view a spectacular display of lights. What are these lights called? Which of the earth's spheres is responsible for producing them? (Lesson 2)

    The lights are called aurora australis, or southern lights. They are produced in the magnetosphere.

3. Use latitude and longitude to tell the location of the following sites to the nearest 5 degrees (Lesson 3)

    a. Amery Ice Shelf   Amery Ice Shelf: 70° S and 75° E

    b. Esperanza Station   Esperanza Station: 65° S and 60° W

    c. Weddell Sea   Weddell Sea 75° S, 45° W

4. View the topographic map of Antarctica on screen 8. What is the best use of this type of map? (Lesson 4)

    Topographic maps are useful for understanding features of the land such as its rise and fall, bodies of water, areas of mountains or woods, and locations of roads or trails.

5. Using contour lines, describe the rise and fall of the land in Antarctica. (Lesson 4)

    Antarctica rises steadily from the coast and forms a peak in the middle of the continent at a height of 4,000 meters. Mountains exist along the southern coast of Antarctica as well.

6. Which type of weathering is more likely to occur in Antarctica: ice wedging or root pry? Explain. (Lesson 5)

    Ice wedging; Antarctica's land surface is affected more by ice than by plants with strong roots to break up rock.

7. Chemical weathering occurs faster in warm, tropical climates, although it happens in cold climates as well. Describe some conditions in Antarctica that could lead to chemical weathering. (Lesson 5)

   Antarctica can support lichen, and acids in lichen roots can chemically weather rock.

8. How might chemical weathering make it easy for mechanical weathering to occur? (Lesson 5)

   Chemical weathering from lichen may create holes in rock. Ice may then form in the holes and mechanically break up rock.

9. Describe the porosity and permeability of Antarctic soil. (Lesson 7)

   Antarctic soil is silty-sandy, so it has low porosity and high permeability. It does not hold a lot of water.

10. How does Antarctic soil differ from soil found in warmer, wetter climates? (Lesson 8)
    Antarctic soil has very little organic matter and cannot hold much water, so it is difficult for plant life to survive. Soil in warmer, wetter climates has more nutrients and can support more plants.

Learning Coach Guide
Lesson 12: Earth's Surface Unit Assessment

Your student will take the Earth's Surface Unit Assessment.

Lesson Objectives

- Describe the basic components of the Earth's physical systems: the atmosphere, biosphere, lithosphere, hydrosphere, and magnetosphere.
- Explain latitude and longitude and recognize them as providing a primary coordinate system for reference to places on the earth.
- Describe features on maps such as coordinate systems, scales, directional indicators, keys, symbols, and contour lines.
- Describe specific uses of topographic maps.
- Describe the major processes that break apart and move material around on the earth's surface to form soil from rock and organic material and to change the shape of the surface.
- Describe major agents of mechanical weathering and of chemical weathering, how the agents cause each kind of weathering, and how mechanical weathering and chemical weathering interact to enhance each other's effects.
- Describe major types of soil in terms of porosity, permeability, and climates in which they are found.

PREPARE

Approximate lesson time is 60 minutes.

ASSESS

Unit Assessment: Earth's Surface Unit Assessment, Part 1 (*Online*)

Students will complete an online assessment of the objectives covered so far in this unit. The assessment will be scored by the computer. The attached answer key is the most current and may not coincide with previously printed guides.

Unit Assessment: Earth's Surface Unit Assessment, Part 2 (*Offline*)

Students will complete this part of the Unit Assessment offline. Print the assessment and have students complete it on their own. Use the answer key to score the assessment, and then enter the results online. The attached answer key is the most current and may not coincide with previously printed guides.

Learning Coach Guide
Lesson 1: Identifying Minerals and Crystals

Think of the role that rocks play in our daily lives. Rocks are used to construct buildings and pave our roads. They contain many important natural resources, including oil, coal, iron, and salt. Look deeper into rocks, and you will see that almost all of them are made of minerals. In this unit, your student will learn how to identify different rocks and minerals, explain how they form, and describe how they are used in everyday life.

If you could slice up a rock and place a very thin section under a microscope, you would see that it is actually made up of a lot of smaller pieces. These smaller pieces are minerals. Studying minerals helps us understand and classify rocks. Your student will learn properties of minerals and will learn different ways to identify minerals.

Lesson Objectives

- Describe how geologists classify rocks and minerals.
- Distinguish rocks from minerals.
- Give examples of observable properties used to identify minerals.

PREPARE

Approximate lesson time is 60 minutes.

Materials

> For the Student
>> 🖳 Mineral Crossword Puzzle
>
> For the Adult
>> 🖳 Mineral Crossword Puzzle Answer Key

Keywords and Pronunciation

chemical properties : properties of a substance relating to the chemical nature and reactivity of a substance

cleavage (KLEE-vij) : the tendency of a mineral to split, when struck, along specific planes of the crystal structure

crystalline (KRIS-tuh-luhn) : made of crystal; containing a repeating structure of atoms

fracture (FRAK-chuhr) : breakage of a mineral, when struck, in a way that is not along cleavage planes of the crystal structure

hardness : the ability of a mineral to resist being scratched

luster : a description of a mineral based on how much light reflects off it

metallic (muh-TA-lik) : a description of the shiny luster of metals

mineral : a naturally occurring, inorganic substance with a specific chemical composition and crystal structure

opaque (oh-PAYK) : not transparent; light is unable to pass through

ore : a rock that contains a mineral that can be mined for profit

physical properties : properties of a substance that can be observed without changing the chemical makeup of the substance

silicate (SIH-luh-kayt) : any of a group of common minerals, such as quartz or feldspar, that make up 90 percent of the earth's crust

streak : a line of finely powdered mineral of characteristic color left when the mineral is rubbed across an unglazed porcelain tile

---

TEACH

Activity 1: Foundations *(Online)*

Instructions

Use this screen as a quick practice to see how much your student already knows about minerals.

Activity 2: Minerals and Crystals *(Online)*

Instructions

In this section, students will read about minerals and ways to identify minerals. Minerals can be identified by crystalline structure, color, steak tests, luster, or by how it breaks. Your student will read about these and other properties of minerals.

Activity 3: Mineral Crossword Puzzle *(Offline)*

Instructions

A crossword puzzle provides a fun way for your student to review terms and definitions related to the lesson. Your student will review key concepts by completing the crossword puzzle.

ASSESS

Lesson Assessment: Identifying Minerals and Crystals, Part 1 (*Online*)

Students will complete an online assessment based on the lesson objectives. The assessment will be scored by the computer. The attached answer key is the most current and may not coincide with previously printed guides.

Lesson Assessment: Identifying Minerals and Crystals, Part 2 (*Offline*)

Students will complete an offline assessment based on the lesson objectives. Print the assessment and have students complete it on their own. Use the answer key to score the assessment, and then enter the results online. The attached answer key is the most current and may not coincide with previously printed guides.

Name _____   Date _____

Mineral Crossword Puzzle Answer Key

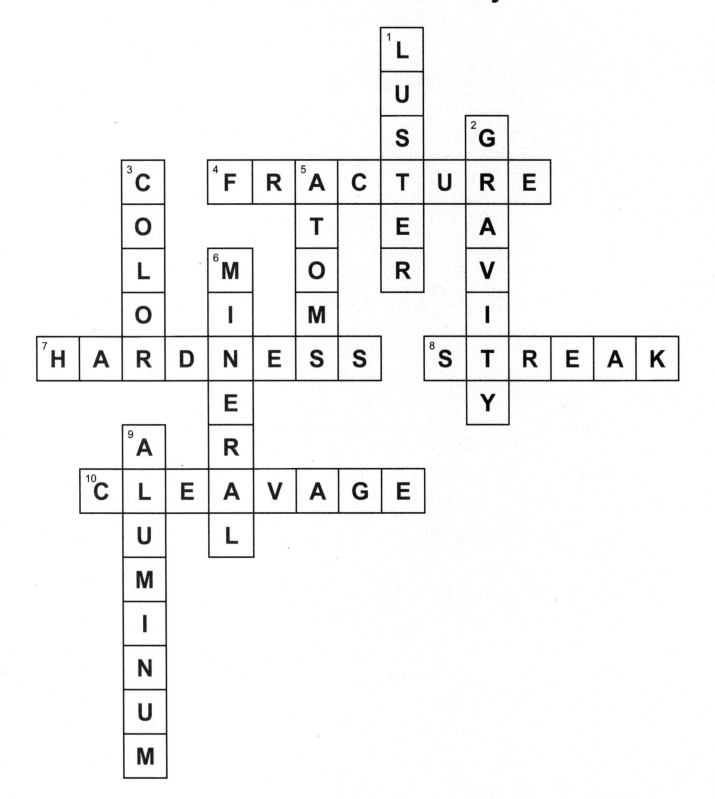

Name _____   Date _____

Identifying Minerals and Crystals, Part 2 Lesson Assessment Answer Key

(15 pts.)

1. Using gabbro as an example, explain what makes gabbro a rock and not a mineral.

    Gabbro is made of several minerals, including feldspars, pyroxene, and olivine. Every gabbro

    rock looks different because the chemical composition and structure varies with each sample.

    _____

    _____

(15 pts.)

2. List the observable properties that scientists use to identify minerals. Explain why chemical properties are not always used to identify minerals.

    Observable properties are: color and streak, luster, cleavage and fracture (crystalline

    structure), and hardness.

    Testing the chemical properties of a mineral might damage the mineral sample. Also, these

    tests can be complex and may require expensive equipment.

    _____

    _____

Learning Coach Guide
Lesson 2: Lab: Mineral Identification

Your student has learned a lot about the basic building blocks on the earth's surface—minerals. She will now have the opportunity to test for various properties to identify minerals on her own.

Lesson Objectives

- Record scientific data using charts, graphs, and/or written descriptions.
- Identify minerals based on color, streak, hardness, and unique properties.
- Record scientific data using charts, graphs, and/or written descriptions.

PREPARE

Approximate lesson time is 60 minutes.

Advance Preparation

- You will need an eyedropper for this lesson. If you do not have an eyedropper, visit a local pharmacy and explain that you need one for a science project. They may be able to supply one free of charge. As an alternative, you may wish to use a regular drinking straw.
- The hardness test for minerals requires the use of a piece of glass. If glass is not available, the edge of a mirror will suffice. Please be aware, however, that some minerals may scratch the mirror and cause permanent damage to its surface.

Materials

For the Student
- 🖳 Data Table
- 🖳 Mineral Identification Lab
- eyedropper
- glass, piece
- magnet
- magnifying glass
- nail, iron
- penny
- Rock and Mineral Kit
- streak plate
- vinegar, distilled white

For the Adult
- 🖳 Lab Answer Key

Keywords and Pronunciation

cleavage (KLEE-vij) : the tendency of a mineral to split, when struck, along specific planes of the crystal structure

fracture (FRAK-chuhr) : breakage of a mineral, when struck, in a way that is not along cleavage planes of the crystal structure

luster : a description of a mineral based on how much light reflects off it

streak : a line of finely powdered mineral of characteristic color left when the mineral is rubbed across an unglazed porcelain tile

---

TEACH
Activity 1: Mineral Identification Lab (Online)

Instructions

This hands-on lab challenges your student to identify various mineral samples by testing their properties.

Safety

Be careful while testing for hardness of the minerals, as it is possible to cut or scratch yourself with the iron nail and glass.

ASSESS

Lesson Assessment: Lab: Mineral Identification (Online)

Review your student's responses on the Mineral Identification Lab and input the results online. The attached answer key is the most current and may not coincide with previously printed guides.

Name _____   Date _____

Mineral Identification Lab Answer Key

Introduction

One of the most important scientific skills is observing. Being a good observer means more than noticing things with your eyes. Observing in science involves all of your senses.

When scientists work with minerals, they may use sight, touch, and even smell to determine the identity of a mineral sample. There are many properties that can be observed and used to identify minerals. Some properties you have studied are:

- color
- luster
- streak
- hardness
- cleavage

In this lab, you will practice making observations by investigating the properties of several mineral samples. Then you will identify each mineral based on your observations.

Hypothesis

Before you conduct a scientific test, you should think about what you predict will happen. Take a few minutes now to observe Samples 7, 13, 23, 25, and 27. Which sample or samples do you think will be hardest? Which sample or samples do you think will have a yellow streak?

Materials

Supplied

Rock and Mineral Kit

magnifying glass or hand lens

streak plate

magnet

Not Supplied

eyedropper

penny

nail

glass

white vinegar

 **Safety Stop**

Have you read the safety information for this lab activity? If not, return to the lesson and do so now.

Name _____   Date _____

Procedure

Watch the *Testing an Unknown Mineral* video to collect data for sample 26.

Observation 1: Color

Examine Sample 13 and observe its color. Record it in the Mineral Identification Data Table.

Observation 2: Streak

Scrape the sample across the streak plate and observe the color of its streak. Record the color in the data table.

Observation 3: Cleavage or Fracture

Observe the edges of the sample. Does the sample show cleavage, meaning that its edges are broken in flat planes? Or does it just show fracture, meaning that the edges are broken irregularly? Watch the *Breaking Minerals* video and then check your observations with those listed in the data table.

Observation 4: Hardness

The diagram below shows how some common materials compare in terms of hardness. Scientists use a numbered scale called the Mohs Hardness Scale to rate the hardness of minerals. Minerals range in hardness from 1 (talc) to 10 (diamond).

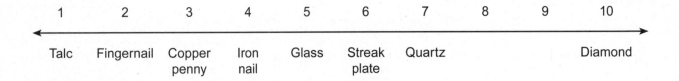

Start by trying to scratch the sample with your fingernail, and then move up to harder objects if you need to (you do not have to scratch the sample with a diamond). The sample will be scratched by objects with a higher hardness. The sample will scratch objects with a lower hardness.

How do you know if your sample has been scratched? After scratching, try to wipe the scratch away with your finger. If the scratch disappears, the sample was not actually scratched. Record the hardness in the data table.

Observation 5: Magnetism

Touch the sample with the magnet. Observe if it is attracted to the magnet.

Observation 6: Fizz Test

Use the eyedropper to carefully place a few drops of white vinegar on the sample. If any bubbles form, make a note of it in the column labeled fizz test in your data table.

Observation 7: Luster

Note if the mineral has metallic or nonmetallic luster.

Repeat Observations 1–7 for samples 7, 23, 25, and 27. Record your observations in the data table, and then complete the analysis section of the lab.

Name _____   Date _____

Analysis

Now you will use your observations to identify each mineral. Use the Mineral Identification Key below and your notes.

Mineral Identification Key						
Mineral Name	Color	Streak	Cleavage or Fracture	Hardness	Luster	Special Properties
Graphite	Black	Iron black	Fracture	1–2	Metallic	Feels greasy, can mark paper
Magnetite	Black	Black	Fracture	6	Metallic	Magnetic
Hematite	Black or red	Red-brown	Fracture	1–6.5	Metallic	Magnetic
Galena	Lead-gray	Gray-black	Cleavage	2.5–3	Metallic	Heavy
Talc	White, gray, green	White	Cleavage	1	Nonmetallic	Feels greasy
Sulfur	Pale yellow	Pale yellow	Fracture	1.5–2.5	Nonmetallic	Rotten-egg odor
Halite	Colorless, red, white	White	Cleavage	2.5	Nonmetallic	None
Calcite	Any color, usually white	White	Cleavage	3	Nonmetallic	Fizzes in acids
Quartz	Clear, white, rose, violet, black	White	Fracture	7	Nonmetallic	None
Mica	Clear, brown, green, yellow	Yellow	Cleavage	2.5	Nonmetallic	None

Sample 7: quartz _____

Sample 13: calcite _____

Sample 23: mica _____

Sample 25: hematite _____

Sample 26: galena _____

Sample 27: sulfur _____

Name   Date

Conclusion

1. Give two examples of minerals that have a property in common.

   Mica and calcite show cleavage. Several minerals have about the same hardness. Calcite and quartz show produce white streaks. Sulfur and mica have yellow streaks.

2. Could you have identified any of the minerals after having described only a few, rather than all, of the properties you tested? If so, give an example.

   Yes. Answers regarding which minerals could have been identified will vary but may include:

   Sulfur; it could have been identified by its color, streak, and smell. Calcite; it could have been identified by its reaction with vinegar. Quartz; it could have been identified by its hardness.

3. Why is it still a good idea to test more properties than might be necessary?

   Because there might be a mistake in some of the observations. Additional testing can help build more consistent information.

Name _____   Date _____

Lab: Mineral Identification Lesson Assessment Answer Key

Answers:

1. Answers will vary. Review your student's responses in the Mineral Identification Lab Data Table to determine if the lab procedures were followed in order to gather all pertinent data from the experiment.

2. Sample 7: __quartz_____
    Sample 13: __calcite_____
    Sample 23: __mica_____
    Sample 25: __hematite_____
    Sample 26: __galena_____
    Sample 27: __sulfur_____

3. To determine whether your student was able to successfully draw conclusions based on the data gathered during the lab experiment, refer to the **Conclusion** answers on the Mineral Identification Lab Answer Key. Answers to the questions will vary but should include similar ideas to those on the Answer Key.

Learning Coach Guide
Lesson 3: Igneous Rocks

Look closely at the rocks around you and you will see that they are not all the same. Find out how observing one type of rock can tell you about its dramatic past.

Lesson Objectives
- Explain how igneous rocks are formed.
- Compare and contrast magma and lava.

PREPARE

Approximate lesson time is 60 minutes.

Materials

For the Student
- 🖳 Igneous Rock Cards
- markers or crayons
- Rock and Mineral Kit
- scissors
- websites listed in Unit Resources
- 🖳 Igneous Rocks Lesson Review

For the Adult
- 🖳 Igneous Rock Cards Answer Key
- 🖳 Igneous Rocks Lesson Review Answer Key

Keywords and Pronunciation

coarse-grained : having a rough texture

crust : the outermost, solid layer of any planet or moon

extrusive rock : fine-grained igneous rock that forms when lava cools quickly at the surface; also called volcanic rock

fine-grained : having a fine, smooth, even texture

igneous rock : rock formed by the cooling and solidification of hot liquid magma or lava

intrusive : coarse-grained igneous rock that cools slowly underground; also called plutonic rock

lava : molten rock or magma that emerges onto the earth´s surface

magma : the molten or partly molten mixture of minerals, gases, and melted rock found below the earth´s surface

texture : the size of individual mineral grains in rock

TEACH
Activity 1: Formed by Fire (Online)
Instructions
Your student will learn that igneous rocks are formed from cooling magma or lava, either inside the earth or on its surface.

Activity 2: Igneous Rock File (Offline)
Instructions
Your student will observe rocks in the Advanced Rock and Mineral Kit and create a Rock File that he will add to in future lessons.

Activity 3: Igneous Rock (Offline)
Instructions
In this activity, your student will review the concepts learned in this lesson. Store the review sheet in your student's Science Notebook.

ASSESS
Lesson Assessment: Igneous Rocks (Online)
Students will complete an online assessment based on the lesson objectives. The assessment will be scored by the computer. The attached answer key is the most current and may not coincide with previously printed guides.

Name _____   Date _____

Igneous Rock Cards Answer Key

By now you know that geologists can study rocks to find out how they were formed. Study some of the igneous rocks in your Rock and Mineral Kit and use the Unit Resources to fill out the Special Features section of the Igneous Rock Cards.

Cut out the cards and start your own Rock File. Use the blank rock file card to add information to your Rock File if you observe more rocks. You may even want to keep your rock records on the computer or start a Rockhound club by collecting rocks, minerals, or fossils in your area.

Materials

- Granite (sample 6)
- Basalt (sample 8)
- Pumice (sample 17)
- Rhyolite (sample 19)
- Obsidian (sample 20)
- Markers/crayons
- Scissors
- Websites found in Unit Resources

Some suggested information for the special features section of each card is listed below. Check your student's work for accuracy and help create a Rock File using the rock cards.

Granite: coarse-grained, nearly always massive, hard and tough; used as a building material

Basalt: fine-grained, can form natural columns that look man-made; see Giant's Causeway on the northern coast of Ireland

Pumice: appears bubbly from gas bubbles escaping from cooling lava; is a rock that will float but eventually will become full of water and sink

Obsidian: Obsidian is a glass and has no mineral crystals because it cools too quickly; used by native cultures to make arrowheads and blades

Rhyolite: looks very different depending on how it erupts; fast eruptions could produce pumice, slower ones could produce obsidian

Name _____   Date _____

Igneous Rocks Lesson Review Answer Key

1. coarse

2. magma, lava

3. fine

4. intrusive, extrusive

5. texture

6. molten

7. The answer should include the concept that coarse-grained rocks are formed by cooling slowly below the earth's surface, whereas fine-grained rocks are formed by cooling quickly at or above the earth's surface.

Learning Coach Guide
Lesson 4: Sedimentary Rocks

Weathering and erosion from wind, running water, or ice create tiny pieces of rock that come together to form other rocks. In this lesson, your student will learn how sedimentary rocks are formed and how they are classified, and he will complete cards for a Rock File.

Lesson Objectives

- Explain how sediment is formed.
- Describe the processes by which sediment becomes sedimentary rock.
- Describe features in sedimentary rocks that help geologists determine the environments in which the rocks formed.

PREPARE

Approximate lesson time is 60 minutes.

Materials

For the Student

- 🖥 Sedimentary Rock Cards
- hammer
- markers or crayons
- Rock and Mineral Kit
- scissors
- sock
- websites listed in Unit Resources
- 🖥 Sedimentary Rocks Lesson Review

For the Adult

- 🖥 Sedimentary Rock Card Answer Key
- 🖥 Sedimentary Rocks Lesson Review Answer Key

Keywords and Pronunciation

cementation : the process of binding particles of rocks

clastic sedimentary rock : rock formed as a result of high pressure on rock fragments and other rocks

compaction : crushing or pressing

conglomerate (kuhn-GLAHM-ruht) : a sedimentary rock made up of large particles, such as pebbles and sand

coquina (koh-KEE-nuh) : soft porous limestone, made of fragments of shells and coral

fossil (FAH-suhl) : the remains of ancient living things

limestone : a common sedimentary rock consisting mostly of calcium carbonate

sandstone : a sedimentary rock formed by the compaction of sand and held together by a natural cement

sediment : loose rock fragments, grains of rock or sand, minerals, or shells and remains of small living things

sedimentary rock : rock formed when sediments are compressed and squeezed together

shale : rock composed of layers of claylike, fine-grained sediment

TEACH
Activity 1: Squeezing Sediment (Online)
Instructions
Your student will explain that sediments form when rocks and organic materials are weathered into smaller fragments and that sedimentary rocks are formed from these materials. Certain features in sedimentary rocks help geologists determine the environments in which the rocks formed.

Activity 2: Sedimentary Rock File (Offline)
Instructions
During this activity your student will gather information about sedimentary rocks. Encourage your student to continue studying sedimentary rocks by adding to the Rock File using the blank sedimentary rock card.

Activity 3: Sedimentary Rocks (Offline)
Instructions
In this activity, your student will review the concepts learned in this lesson. Store the review sheet in your student's Science Notebook.

ASSESS

Lesson Assessment: Sedimentary Rocks (Online)
Students will complete an online assessment based on the lesson objectives. The assessment will be scored by the computer. The attached answer key is the most current and may not coincide with previously printed guides.

Name _____   Date _____

Sedimentary Rock Cards Answer Key

How confident are you that you can "read" rocks? Try it by examining a few of the sedimentary rocks in your Rock and Mineral kit and answering the questions below. Then, complete the Special Features section of the Sedimentary Rock Cards, cut them out and add them to your Rock File. Use the blank rock file card to add information to your Rock File if you observe more rocks.

Want to see the crystals in your geode? Place the geode in a sock and hit it very lightly with a hammer. Your geode may not break perfectly in half, but you should be able to see crystals when it breaks into pieces.

Materials

- Sandstone (sample 5)
- Chert (sample 22)
- Mudstone (sample 31)
- Geode (sample 36)
- hammer
- sock
- markers/crayons
- scissors
- Websites from Unit Resources

Some suggested information for the Special features section of each card is listed below. Check your student's work for accuracy and help create a Rock File using the rock cards.

Chert: Some ancient cherts contain fossils of a type of one-celled organism that lives in the ocean. (They are visible only with a microscope.) Chert was used in ancient cultures to make arrowheads, spears, and knives.

Sandstone: Sandstone is often used for building.

Mudstone: This rock is made of very thin layers, about as thick as pages in a book.

Geode: Inside a geode, minerals dissolved in water form crystals where water flows through the rock's open space. A geode can be cut in half to see many colors of crystals.

Name _____   Date _____

Sedimentary Rocks Lesson Review Answer Key

Answers

1. 3, 4, 1, 5, 2

2. C, D, F, A

Learning Coach Guide
Lesson 5: Metamorphic Rocks

Imagine rocks compressed down to a fraction of their original size, changing from one form to another. Your student will learn that heat and pressure are involved in forming metamorphic rock from igneous, sedimentary, and even other metamorphic rock. This lesson will prepare your student to discuss the components of the rock cycle.

Lesson Objectives

- Explain how metamorphic rocks are formed.
- Give examples of metamorphic rocks and describe how they formed.

PREPARE

Approximate lesson time is 60 minutes.

Materials

For the Student

    💻 Metamorphic Rock Cards

    markers or crayons

    Rock and Mineral Kit

    scissors

    websites listed in Unit Resources

    💻 Lesson Review

For the Adult

    💻 Metamorphic Rock Cards Answer Key

    💻 Lesson Review Answer Key

Keywords and Pronunciation

foliated (FOH-lee-ay-tuhd) : relating to rock that has a layered structure

gneiss (niys) : foliated metamorphic rock, usually of the same composition as granite

marble : metamorphic rock formed by alteration of limestone, used especially in architecture and sculpture

metamorphic rock (meh-tuh-MOR-fik) : rock that has undergone change, caused by intense heat and pressure, from an earlier form, without melting

metamorphosis (meh-tuh-MOR-fuh-suhs) : change of physical form, structure, or substance

nonfoliated rock : metamorphic rock that does not separate into layers when broken

quartzite : metamorphic rock formed from quartz sandstone

schist (shist) : flaky metamorphic rock formed from clay and mud, composed of minerals such as mica, talc, hornblende, and graphite

slate : fine-grained metamorphic rock, formed from shale that splits into thin, smooth-surfaced layers

TEACH
Activity 1: Hard Pressed *(Online)*
Instructions
Your student will explore the processes involved in forming metamorphic rock. She will also explore features of specific metamorphic rocks.

Activity 2: Metamorphic Rock File *(Offline)*
Instructions
During this activity, your student will gather information about sedimentary rocks. Encourage her to continue studying metamorphic rocks by adding to the Rock File using the blank metamorphic rock card.

Activity 3: Metamorphic Rocks *(Offline)*
Instructions
In this activity, your student will review the concepts learned in this lesson. Store the review sheet in your student's Science Notebook.

ASSESS
Lesson Assessment: Metamorphic Rocks (*Online*)
Students will complete an online assessment based on the lesson objectives. The assessment will be scored by the computer. The attached answer key is the most current and may not coincide with previously printed guides.

Name _____   Date _____

Metamorphic Rock Cards Answer Key

Complete your Rock File by adding information about metamorphic rocks to rock cards. Examine samples in your Rock and Mineral Kit. Then complete the Special features section of the metamorphic rock cards, cut them out, and add them to your Rock File. Use the blank file card to add information to your Rock File if you observe more rocks.

Materials

- gneiss (sample 2)
- slate (sample 4)
- marble (sample 9)
- quartzite (sample 29)
- markers/crayons
- scissors
- websites from Unit Resources

Gneiss

Contains: feldspar, mica, quartz (the same minerals as granite)

Where found/how formed: can be formed from sedimentary rock such as sandstone or shale or from igneous rock such as granite; can be found in Arizona

Special features:

Gneiss has alternating layers of minerals and is often used as a paving stone.

_____

_____

_____

_____

Draw a picture of gneiss above.

Name _____   Date _____

Slate

Contains: quartz, muscovite, clay, volcanic ash

Where found/how formed: derived from shale that has undergone low pressure and temperatures; can be found in Pennsylvania, Vermont, and New York

Special features:

Slate has been used for headstones and

chalkboards.

_____

_____

_____

_____

Draw a picture of slate above.

Marble

Contains: calcite (which is also found in limestone)

Where found/how formed: metamorphosed from limestone or dolomite; can be found in Vermont, Tennessee, Missouri, Georgia, and Alabama

Special features:

Marble is used as a building material; it

can be used for bathtubs and sink tops.

Many statues are carved from marble.

_____

_____

Draw a picture of marble above.

Name _____   Date _____

Quartzite

Contains: quartz, silica

Where found/how formed: heating of and pressure on sandstone; can be found in South Dakota, Minnesota, Arizona, and Utah

Special features:

Quartzite can vary in color depending on

the minerals present; it is also one of the

hardest rocks known.

_____

_____

_____

Draw a picture of quartzite above.

_____

Contains:

_____

Where found/how formed:

_____

_____

Special features:

_____

_____

_____

_____

_____

Draw a picture of the rock above.

Name _____   Date _____

Metamorphic Rocks Lesson Review Answer Key

Review what you have learned about metamorphic rocks. When finished, place your completed lesson review sheet in your Science Notebook.

Vocabulary Crossword

Read each clue and fill in the puzzle with the term that is described.

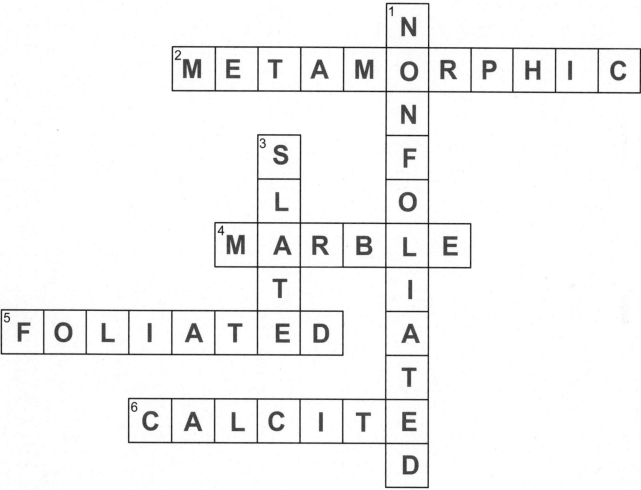

Across

2. Rock that has changed form from heat and pressure
4. A type of metamorphic rock formed from limestone
5. Metamorphic rock that splits into sheets when broken
6. A mineral found in both limestone and marble

Down

1. Metamorphic rock that does not split into sheets when broken
3. A type of metamorphic rock formed from shale

Learning Coach Guide
Lesson 6. Optional: Your Choice

Lesson Objectives

- Practice skills and reinforce concepts taught in this course.

PREPARE

Approximate lesson time is 60 minutes.

Learning Coach Guide
Lesson 7: The Rock Cycle

It's hard to believe, but rocks are always changing. You may know that igneous and sedimentary rocks can turn into metamorphic rocks with heat and pressure. But did you know that a metamorphic rock can eventually become a sedimentary or igneous rock? Rocks are formed, moved, and transformed in the rock cycle. Your student will learn about the different phases in the rock cycle.

Lesson Objectives

- Summarize how the earth's surface materials are constantly formed, reformed, and transformed from one type of rock into another through the processes of the rock cycle.
- Relate the rock cycle to the formation of layers of rock.
- Describe the arrangement of rocks in rock layers.

PREPARE

Approximate lesson time is 60 minutes.

Materials

For the Student

📖 All About Rocks

For the Adult

📖 All About Rocks Answer Key

Keywords and Pronunciation

igneous rock : rock formed by the cooling and solidification of hot liquid magma or lava

metamorphic rock (meh-tuh-MOR-fik) : rock that has undergone change, caused by intense heat and pressure, from an earlier form, without melting

sediment : loose rock fragments, grains of rock or sand, minerals, or shells and remains of small living things

sedimentary rock : rock formed when sediments are compressed and squeezed together

TEACH
Activity 1: The Rock Cycle (Online)
Instructions

Your student has learned a lot about rocks and minerals. In this lesson, your student will learn about how different rocks are formed in the rock cycle.

Activity 2: All About Rocks *(Online)*

Instructions

Your student will fill out the passage with terms in the Word Bank. Your student may refer back to the lesson for the answers.

ASSESS

Lesson Assessment: The Rock Cycle, Part 1 (*Online*)

Students will complete an online assessment based on the lesson objectives. The assessment will be scored by the computer. The attached answer key is the most current and may not coincide with previously printed guides.

Lesson Assessment: The Rock Cycle, Part 2 (*Offline*)

Students will complete an offline assessment based on the lesson objectives. Print the assessment and have students complete it on their own. Use the answer key to score the assessment, and then enter the results online. The attached answer key is the most current and may not coincide with previously printed guides.

Name _____   Date _____

All About Rocks Answer Key

Fill in each blank below with a term from the Word Bank. You will use each term once, and you will use all of the terms.

Word Bank

metamorphic rock	temperatures	rock cycle
sedimentary rock	thousands to millions	magma
igneous rock	weathering and erosion	

The series of pathways by which a rock may change from one type into another is called the

_____ rock cycle _____. One part of the cycle includes the weathering and erosion of rocks

into sediment. Sediment eventually forms _____ sedimentary rock _____ layers that may change

into metamorphic or igneous rocks. For example, a sedimentary rock that undergoes high heat and

high pressure may change into a _____ metamorphic rock _____. Even higher _____ temperatures _____

lead to melting of rock and formation of _____ magma _____. When magma cools,

_____ igneous rock _____ is formed. _____ Weathering and erosion _____ of sedimentary, igneous, and

metamorphic rocks lead to the formation of sediment and, eventually, new sedimentary rocks. Due to

the dynamic processes that occur on and below the earth's surface, it is common for rocks to change

from one type into another. However, it takes _____ thousands to millions _____ of years for these changes

to occur.

Name _____ Date _____

The Rock Cycle, Part 2 Lesson Assessment Answer Key

Use the lines provided to answer each question.

(10 pts.)

1. Describe how mudstone forms.

   Flowing rivers carry sediment and empty into the ocean, where a river's sediment slows

   down and eventually settles to the ocean bottom and, over time, creates horizontal layers.

   As these layers build up and become compressed, water is squeezed out and rock called

   mudstone forms.

(10 pts.)

2. What are the main agents of change in the rock cycle?

   temperature, pressure, weathering, and erosion

(10 pts.)

3. Although it is rare, one type of rock can be changed into a different type of rock very quickly.
   Explain and give examples of how this could happen.

   When a meteorite strikes the earth, the sudden increase in temperature and pressure can

   quickly change the surrounding rock into metamorphic rock. When a volcano erupts, the

   magma and exploding materials can fall back onto the earth's surface as sediments. When

   a heat wave occurs, rapid evaporation may occur from small bodies of water, leaving behind

   minerals such as halite.

Learning Coach Guide
Lesson 8: Lab: Rock Cycle

In this lesson, your student will further explore the rock cycle using samples from the Rock and Mineral Kit.

Lesson Objectives

- Identify sources of information used in scientific research.
- Distinguish rocks from minerals.
- Give examples of observable properties used to identify minerals.

PREPARE

Approximate lesson time is 60 minutes.

Materials

For the Student

📖 Rocks and the Rock Cycle

Rock and Mineral Kit

For the Adult

📖 Rocks and the Rock Cycle Answer Key

TEACH
Activity 1: Review the Rock Cycle (Online)

Instructions
Students will complete the Rock Cycle Lab using their Rock and Mineral Kit.

Activity 2: Rocks and the Rock Cycle Lab (Online)

Instructions
Use the rock kit and the lab sheet to complete the Rock Cycle Lab.

ASSESS

Lesson Assessment: Lab: Rock Cycle (Online)

Review your student's responses on the Rocks and the Rock Cycle Lab and input the results online. The attached answer key is the most current and may not coincide with previously printed guides.

Name   Date

Rocks and the Rock Cycle Lab Answer Key

The rock cycle explains what we know about how rocks form and change. It also helps scientists explain the appearance of rocks. In this activity, you will have a chance to actually place rocks in the rock cycle, make observations about the rocks, and draw conclusions about rock types. Use books, magazines, lessons, websites, or other scientific resources to find information to complete this lab.

Materials

construction paper

markers and/or crayons

gneiss, sample 2

slate, sample 4

sandstone, sample 5

granite, sample 6

basalt, sample 8

marble, sample 9

shale, sample 10

coquina, sample 11

conglomerate, sample 14

coal, sample 16

pumice, sample 17

limestone, sample 18

rhyolite, sample 19

obsidian, sample 20

diatomite, sample 21

chert, sample 22

graphite, sample 24

gabbro, sample 28

quartzite, sample 29

mudstone, sample 31

geode, sample 36

1. Using construction paper and colored pens, and referring to the rock cycle diagram online, create a rock cycle diagram showing each of the following:

    a. igneous rocks

    b. metamorphic rocks

    c. sedimentary rocks

    d. where erosion takes place

    e. where weathering takes place

    f. locations of volcanic activity

    g. where heat and pressure transform rocks

    h. where compaction and cementation occur

    i. other important phases in the rock cycle

2. Now that you have created your rock cycle diagram, take each rock (not mineral) and place it in the correct place in the rock cycle, sorting by rock type (sedimentary, igneous, metamorphic). Then, look at each group of rocks and complete the tables on pages 2 and 3.

    The following rocks from the K12 Rock and Mineral Kit can be sorted as follows. The numbers in parentheses correspond with the numbers in your Rock and Mineral Kit. Not all rocks will be used because many are classified as minerals.

Name _____   Date _____

3. Use books, websites, lessons, or other scientific resources to complete this table. Suggested answers are below. Your student may have found different similar characteristics among minerals.

Name of Igneous Rock	Description of Rock	Possible Origin of Rock	Similar Characteristics with Rocks in this Group
basalt (8)	gray and fine-grained	volcanic material	extrusive, formed at earth's surface
granite (6)	red, black, crystalline	volcanic material	intrusive, formed below earth's surface
obsidian (20)	black and glassy	volcanic material	extrusive, formed at earth's surface
pumice (17)	white and very light	volcanic material	extrusive, formed at earth's surface

Name of Metamorphic Rock	Description of Rock	Possible Origin of Rock	Similar Characteristics with Rocks in this Group
gneiss (2)	light and dark: crystalline		foliated, like slate
slate (4)	gray: layered	mud	foliated, like gneiss
marble (9)	white and crystalline	quartz	none
quartzite (29)	multi-crystalline		crystalline

Name of Sedimentary Rock	Description of Rock	Possible Origin of Rock	Similar Characteristics with Rocks in this Group
fossil (1)	yellow conglomerate		similar to diatomite
sandstone (5)	layered red: rough	sand	rough like others
coquina (11)	conglomerate	shells	conglomerate
diatomite (21)	chalky		similar to limestone

Name _____   Date _____

Observations

4. Complete the table to describe and compare rock types. Using your observations from the previous chart and your rock kit, compare and contrast the different types of rocks in the table below.

Rock Types	Igneous vs. Sedimentary	Metamorphic vs. Sedimentary	Metamorphic vs. Igneous
Comparison	The sedimentary rocks seem to be conglomerates of smaller parts; some igneous rocks are crystalline, glassy, or pitted in texture.	The sedimentary rocks seem to be conglomerates of smaller parts; some metamorphic rocks are crystalline.	The rocks are similar in some ways, such as being crystalline. However, obsidian and pumice are distinct from the other rocks.

Analysis

5. How would you describe the characteristics of each rock type? Which characteristics of one or more rocks in each group give clues about how that rock was formed?

    Sedimentary rocks appear to be smaller bits cemented together. Metamorphic rocks and some

    igneous rocks have a crystalline appearance. Slate is layered, and obsidian is glassy or shiny.

Conclusions

6. Choose one rock from your Rock and Mineral Kit. Write a brief history about the origins of this rock type using what you know about the rock cycle. Then, predict what might happen to this rock in the future.

    Answers may vary, but must include where the rock fits into the Rock Cycle.

7. List three sources of information (books, lessons, websites, magazines, etc.) used to conduct this investigation. Include titles, authors, and/or website addresses.

    A. Answers will vary, based on individual research. All sources used should be listed and

    B. citations should be written correctly.

    C. _____

Name _____   Date _____

Lab: Rock Cycle Lesson Assessment Answer Key

Answers:

1. Answers will vary. Review your student's responses in the Rocks and the Rock Cycle lab to determine if the lab procedures were followed in order to gather all pertinent data from the experiment.

2. Refer to the **Analysis** section of your student's Rocks and the Rock Cycle lab. Answers will vary but should include: Sedimentary rocks appear to be smaller bits cemented together. Metamorphic rocks and some igneous rocks have a crystalline appearance. Slate is layered, and obsidian is glassy or shiny.

3. Refer to the **Conclusions** section of your student's Rocks and the Rock Cycle lab. Answers may vary, but must include where the rock fits into the Rock Cycle.

4. Refer to the **Conclusions** section of your student's Rocks and the Rock Cycle lab. Answers will vary, based on individual research. All sources used should be listed and citations should be written correctly.

Learning Coach Guide
Lesson 9: Unit Review

Your student has learned a lot about rocks and minerals. Now take this time for her to review concepts learned in the unit before taking the Unit Assessment.

Lesson Objectives

- Define rocks as composed of minerals and recognize that they are classified as igneous, sedimentary, or metamorphic based on how they were formed.
- Explain how sedimentary rocks are formed and identify features that help determine the type of environment in which they formed.
- Summarize the processes called the rock cycle.
- Explain how metamorphic rocks are formed.
- State the defining characteristics of a mineral.
- Recognize that physical and chemical properties of minerals are a result of the types and arrangements of their atoms.
- Explain how properties of minerals can be used in their identification.
- Explain how igneous rocks form and recognize how physical properties of an igneous rock reveal its origin.

PREPARE

Approximate lesson time is 60 minutes.

Materials

For the Student

    💻 Unit Review

For the Adult

    💻 Unit Review Answer Key

TEACH
Activity 1: Rocks and Minerals *(Online)*
Instructions

This lesson is a review of concepts learned in the previous lessons of the unit.

Name _____ Date _____

Rocks and Minerals Unit Review Answer Key

Review important concepts about rocks and minerals by reviewing the lessons and activities you have completed in this unit. You will need to go back over parts of each lesson to complete the review. Read each question carefully, and then answer it in the space provided.

1. List the mineral properties you tested during the Mineral Identification Lab.

    color, streak, hardness, reaction with vinegar (fizz test) and magnetism

2. Which mineral from the Mineral Identification lab ranked highest in hardness?

    quartz

3. Explain how the arrangements of atoms into crystalline structures help geologists identify minerals.

    A mineral's atoms can be arranged into differently shaped crystals. For example, galena's crystals are cubic while quartz's crystals form a six-sided hexagon. Geologists can study these crystals with magnifying glasses or high-powered microscopes to identify a mineral.

4. Name a mineral and describe three properties that can be used to identify it.

    Answers may vary. Galena is gray-black in color, has a gray streak, and is no harder than a penny (2.5 on the hardness scale). It is not magnetic and does not fizz in vinegar. List the mineral properties you tested during the Mineral Identification Lab.

5. Review the igneous rock animation in the Igneous Rocks lesson. Explain how igneous rocks are formed from magma. Name one example each of an intrusive and extrusive igneous rock.

    Magma that reaches the surface of the earth is called lava. Igneous rocks form from cooling magma or lava. Rocks formed from magma cool slowly underground and have large, coarse grains. Rocks formed from lava cool quickly at the surface and have small, fine grains. Granite is an example of an igneous rock formed below the surface. Obsidian is a rock formed at the earth's surface.

6. Review the sedimentary rock animation in the Sedimentary Rocks lesson. What two things need to happen to turn sediment into rock?

Sediment must be compacted, or pressed together, to form sedimentary rock. And, sediment must undergo cementation, in which particles of sediment become "glued" together.

7. Review the metamorphic rock animation in the Metamorphic Rocks lesson. Describe how metamorphic rock can be formed from igneous, sedimentary, or other metamorphic rocks.

Heat and pressure on any igneous, sedimentary, or metamorphic rock can turn that rock into another metamorphic rock. The rocks' chemical structure is changed and a new rock is formed.

8. Review the rock cycle diagram in the Rock Cycle lesson and the Rock Cycle Lab. If you are unsure of any of the terms, make flashcards to review the processes involved in the rock cycle.

Learning Coach Guide
Lesson 10: Unit Assessment

Your student has learned a lot about rocks and minerals in previous lessons and is now ready to take the Unit Assessment.

Lesson Objectives

- Define rocks as composed of minerals and recognize that they are classified as igneous, sedimentary, or metamorphic based on how they were formed.
- Explain how metamorphic rocks are formed.
- State the defining characteristics of a mineral.
- Recognize that physical and chemical properties of minerals are a result of the types and arrangements of their atoms.
- Explain how properties of minerals can be used in their identification.
- Explain how igneous rocks form and recognize how physical properties of an igneous rock reveal its origin.
- Summarize the processes that are collectively known as the rock cycle.

PREPARE

Approximate lesson time is 60 minutes.

ASSESS

Unit Assessment: Rocks and Minerals, Part 1 (*Online*)

Students will complete an online assessment of the objectives covered so far in this unit. The assessment will be scored by the computer. The attached answer key is the most current and may not coincide with previously printed guides.

Unit Assessment: Rocks and Minerals, Part 2 (*Offline*)

Students will complete this part of the Unit Assessment offline. Print the assessment and have students complete it on their own. Use the answer key to score the assessment, and then enter the results online. The attached answer key is the most current and may not coincide with previously printed guides.

Learning Coach Guide
Lesson 1. Optional: Your Choice

In this unit, your student will explore fossils and how geologists use them to reconstruct the history of the earth. Your student will learn basic principles of how fossils are laid down in sediments, which later turn into sedimentary rock. Building on these principles, your student will learn how geologists determine the age of a fossil and the rock in which it is embedded.

Lesson Objectives
- Practice skills and reinforce concepts taught in this course.

PREPARE

Approximate lesson time is 60 minutes.

Learning Coach Guide
Lesson 2: Linking Past and Present

The work of scientists such as Charles Lyell and James Hutton paved the way for modern geology. This lesson traces the history of geology during the critical period around 1800 when new discoveries were made about our earth and how to interpret its rock layers.

Lesson Objectives
- Explain that the processes that have shaped the earth through geologic time are the same today as they were in the past.
- Summarize major findings of James Hutton and Charles Lyell.

PREPARE

Approximate lesson time is 60 minutes.

Materials
> For the Student
>> 🖳 Rates of Geologic Processes
> For the Adult
>> 🖳 Rates of Geologic Processes Answer Key

Keywords and Pronunciation
erosion : the gradual removal of the surface of the land by water, wind, or glaciers

geology : the study of the earth: how it was formed, what it is made of, and how it changes over time; studying geology is like looking at the history of the earth

sediment : loose rock fragments, grains of rock or sand, minerals, or shells and remains of small living things

uniformitarianism (YOO-nuh-for-muh-TEHR-ee-uh-nih-zuhm) : a principle stating that the geological processes taking place on earth today are the same as those of the past and thus can be used to explain past geological events

uplift : the rise in elevation of a layer of rocks resulting from the application of forces within the earth

weathering : the breakdown of rocks by physical or chemical processes; weathering causes the rocks on a cliff to wear away

---

TEACH
Activity 1: Hutton, Lyell, and Uniformitarianism *(Online)*

Instructions
Your student will learn about the history of geology during the critical period around 1800 when new discoveries were made about our earth and how to interpret its rock layers.

Activity 2: Rates of Geologic Processes *(Offline)*

Instructions
Your student will make predictions about geologic processes occurring over long periods of time.

86

How to Help
If needed, assist your student with the math involved in this activity. Show him how to multiply the measurements by 100 for the first column and 10,000 for the second to find the rates of geologic process for the different lengths of time.

Activity 3: Linking Past and Present *(Offline)*
Instructions
In this activity, your student will review the concepts learned in this lesson. Store the review sheet in your student's Science Notebook.

Answers to Lesson Review
1. Sample answer: The principle of uniformitarianism states that the geologic processes that happened on earth in the past are the same as the ones that are happening today.
2. Sample answer: If geologists understand that the processes happening today are the same as ones that happened in the past, they can study the effects of processes today to determine what their effects might have been in the past. Then, they can look for signs of those effects in rocks to help them infer what was happening on earth in the past.
3. Hutton concluded that the same processes that change earth's surface today also occurred in the past, and that many geologic processes are cyclic.
4. Most geologic processes cause very slow changes. In order for such slow processes to cause large changes in earth's surface, the earth must be very old.
5. Lyell provided evidence to support the principle of uniformitarianism, and helped to make the idea more well known.

ASSESS

Lesson Assessment: Linking Past and Present (*Online*)
Students will complete an online assessment based on the lesson objectives. The assessment will be scored by the computer. The attached answer key is the most current and may not coincide with previously printed guides.

Name _____   Date _____

Rates of Geologic Processes Answer Key

Hutton and Lyell's work was based on the idea that processes and forces that affect earth's surface have acted uniformly (in the same way) since earth formed. Mountains rise, valleys deepen, and sand grains collect now the same way they did long ago.

But earth has changed over time, and that could change the rates at which geologic processes such as erosion, deposition, and uplifting occur. The table below explains the average rate at which some geologic processes occur.

Process	Rate per 1,000 years	After 100,000 years	After 10,000,000 years
Sea level changes	10 m	1000 m	100,000 m
Regional erosion	2 m	200 m	20,000 m
Uplift	10 cm	1,000 cm	100,000 cm

1. Calculate the amount of sea level change, erosion, and uplift for 100,000 years and 10,000,000 years. Remember, 100 cm = 1 m.

    See the table above. _____

2. After 10,000,000 years, how much of earth's surface would be eroded away?

    20,000 m _____

3. After 10,000,000 years, how much uplift would occur?

    100,000 cm _____

4. Which is the fastest process: sea level changes, erosion, or uplift?

    Sea level changes _____

Learning Coach Guide
Lesson 3: Earth's Age

One of the goals of earth science is to give an accurate description of the history of the earth. To do this, scientists have to know the relative ages of rocks and fossils, as well as their ages in absolute years. The process that gives us good estimates of the age of rocks and fossils in absolute years is called *radiometric dating*. Once rock layers are dated, geologists are able to construct a history of the earth and create a geologic time scale.

Lesson Objectives

- Distinguish between absolute and relative dating techniques.
- Explain how geologists use radiometric dating to date rocks and fossils.
- Summarize geologic evidence for estimating the age of the earth.

PREPARE

Approximate lesson time is 60 minutes.

Advance Preparation

- Your student will need a shoebox or other box with a lid. The Rock and Mineral Kit box will work if you remove the sample tray.

Materials

For the Student

    🖳 Determining Half-Life

    cubes, centimeter/gram

    pen, felt-tip

    shoebox with lid

For the Adult

    🖳 Determining Half-Life Answer Key

Keywords and Pronunciation

absolute dating : a way of finding out the actual age of an object or event

fossil (FAH-suhl) : the remains of ancient living things

half-life : the time needed for half of a sample of radioactive material to decay

isotope (IY-suh-tohp) : one of two or more atoms of the same element that have the same number of protons but different numbers of neutrons

radiometric dating : a way of determining the approximate age in years of geologic samples using radioactive isotopes

relative dating : a way of finding out if one object or event is older or younger than another object or event

---

TEACH
Activity 1: A New Way to Date Earth (Online)
Instructions
Radiometric dating uses isotopes to find the exact ages of rocks and fossilized material. Your student will learn about this method, including what half-life is all about and how it is used in dating rocks and fossils. Your student will find out how scientists use relative and absolute dating to uncover and organize the major events in earth's past.

Activity 2: Working with Scientific Data: Determine Half-Life (Offline)
Instructions
To determine half-life, scientists analyze how long it takes for atoms of a particular element to decay. Your student will simulate this process with an imaginary element called Virtualium.

Tips
Your student may wish to demonstrate an understanding of half-life by using a large number of marbles or beans.
After each round, be sure that your student removes half the marbles or beans and correlates this with time.
Errors
Your student can easily be confused by the concept of a half-life. Because students are accustomed to thinking about a lifetime in human terms, it would be easy to say that a man who died at 70 had a half-life of 35 years. But when dealing with radioactivity, the concept is quite different. If an amount of a radioactive isotope has a half-life of 70 years, half of it would be gone after the first 70 years. Then, it would take another 70 years to reduce that remaining amount by half. And it would take another 70 years to reduce that remaining amount by half again. Be very careful that your student does not think about half-life as "half of a lifetime" in human terms.

Activity 3: Earth's Age (Offline)
Instructions
In this activity, your student will review the concepts learned in this lesson. Store the review sheet in your student's Science Notebook.

Answers to Lesson Review
1. True
2. False. Absolute dating methods are useful for figuring out the absolute age of geologic events.
3. True
4. False. The absolute age of geologic events can be determined.
5. True
6. True
7. False. Modern geologists use relative dating methods to support absolute dating methods.
8. False. Rocks found on the moon indicate that earth is about the same age as the moon, about 4.4 to 4.6 billion years old.

ASSESS

Lesson Assessment: Earth's Age, Part 1 (*Online*)

Students will complete an online assessment based on the lesson objectives. The assessment will be scored by the computer. The attached answer key is the most current and may not coincide with previously printed guides.

Lesson Assessment: Earth's Age, Part 2 (*Offline*)

Students will complete an offline assessment based on the lesson objectives. Print the assessment and have students complete it on their own. Use the answer key to score the assessment, and then enter the results online. The attached answer key is the most current and may not coincide with previously printed guides.

Name _____   Date _____

Determining Half-Life Answer Key

How do scientists figure out the age of rocks on earth? Let's take a look at some of their methods.

Relative Dating

Consider the following members of a family: Mother, Father, Grandmother, Son, and Daughter. It is impossible to figure out the exact age of any of the members of this family from just that information. You could draw some probable conclusions, however.

For example, Mother and Father are older than Son and Daughter. They are also likely to be younger than Grandmother. But that's about all you can say. This is an example of relative dating because the ages of the family members are relative but not exact. Relative dating works for rocks, too.

Scientists have recognized that layers of rock have been deposited in sequence, one on top of another. This leads them to conclude that rocks in the bottom layers of undisturbed rock are older than those in the top layers.

Absolute Dating

To find the absolute age of rocks, scientists use radiometric dating. Radiometric dating involves studying the amounts of radioactive isotopes in some material. Do the following activity to explore radiometric dating.

Materials

centimeter/gram cubes (100)

shoebox

felt-tip pen

Procedure

1. Imagine the centimeter gram cubes represent an imaginary element called Virtualium.

2. Mark only one side of each cube with a black marker or felt-tip pen.

3. Place all of the cubes in the box.

4. Hold the lid tightly and turn the box over twice. Remove the lid.

5. Take out all of the cubes that have the marked side up. These cubes represent atoms of Virtualium that have decayed.

6. In the data table, record the total number of cubes removed from the box (remember these are decayed) after each trial. Also record the total number of cubes left in the box.

7. Repeat steps 4 through 6 until you have completed 8 trials or until all of the cubes have been removed.

Data

Record your data in the table.

Data Table

Trial	Amount Decayed	Amount Left
1		
2		
3		
4		
5		
6		
7		
8		

Analysis

Use the information collected in your data table to make a graph. Label the horizontal (across) axis "Trials." Label the vertical (up and down) axis "Number of Atoms Remaining." Make a line graph to show the data in the "Amount Left" column of your Data Table.

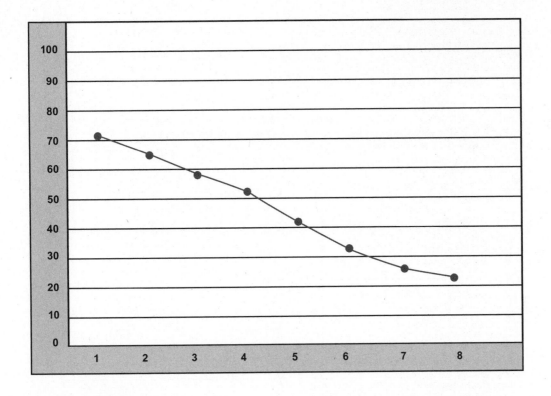

Conclusion

1. How many trials did it take for half of the Virtualium atoms to decay?

   Answers will vary. See student graph. According to this sample, 4 trials.

2. Suppose each trial equals 1,000 years. What is the half-life of Virtualium?

   Answers will vary. See student data. According to this sample, 4,000 years.

3. Suppose each trial equals 1,000 years. After half (50) of the Virtualium cubes were removed from the box, about how long did it take for half of the rest of the cubes to decay?

   Answers will vary. See student graph. According to this sample, about 4,000 years.

4. Imagine you have a radioactive sample containing both Virtualium and decayed atoms of Virtualium. After analysis, you find it contains 10 atoms of Virtualium and 40 decayed atoms. How old is your sample? (Hint: You must use the half-life of Virtualium determined earlier in the activity.)

   Answers will vary. See student graph. According to this sample, about 8,000 years.

Name _____   Date _____

Earth's Age, Part 2 Lesson Assessment Answer Key

Answer the question below.

(10 pts.)

1. List and describe two pieces of evidence for scientists' ideas about the age of earth.

   Answers may vary but should include: earth must be at least as old as its oldest rocks.

   The oldest known earth rocks are 3.7 billion to 3.8 billion years old. Some moon rocks and

   meteorites have been dated as being 4.4 to 4.6 billion years old. Because the solid bodies of

   our solar system probably formed at around the same time, scientists think that the earth is

   about 4.6 billion years old.

Learning Coach Guide
Lesson 4: Fossils

In this lesson, your student will explore fossils and how geologists use them to reconstruct the history of the earth. Your student will learn basic principles of how fossils are laid down in sedimentary rock and will understand the importance of fossils as evidence to past life on earth.

Lesson Objectives

- Describe fossils as recognized remains or traces of preexisting life, which may exist in the form of shells, bones, or impressions of plant leaves and soft body parts.
- Explain that fossils provide evidence of changes on earth over time.

PREPARE

Approximate lesson time is 60 minutes.

Keywords and Pronunciation

body fossil : the remains of a dead organism's actual body parts

excavate : to remove from the ground by digging

fossil (FAH-suhl) : the remains of ancient living things

index fossil : a fossil found to be especially useful in correlating rock layers across large distances

paleontologist (pay-lee-ahn-TAH-luh-jist) : a scientist who studies the history of life on earth as shown in fossils

trace fossil : a fossil formed from the footprints, burrows, or other activities of a living organism

tyrannosaurus (tuh-RAN-uh-SAWR-us) : a large, carnivorous dinosaur

TEACH
Activity 1: Finding Out from Fossils *(Online)*
Instructions
Your student will understand that fossils provide evidence of past life.

Activity 2: Environments of Long Ago *(Offline)*
Instructions
In this activity, your student will learn how fossils can provide clues about paleoenvironments, or environments that existed millions of years ago. Often, fossils indicate that certain places on earth were very different in the past than they are today.

Your student will read about fossils found in Antarctica that lead scientists to believe that its paleoenvironment was different from the frozen land it is today. Your student will describe that paleoenvironment based on the information about Antarctic fossils.

Tips

- Encourage your student to interpret the information about fossils found in Antarctica in order to infer information about its paleoenvironment.
- Provide your student with a reference for a drawing of a duck-billed dinosaur. A link can be found in the Resources tab in the lesson opener.

Answers to Anarctic Fossils Activity

1. Iystrosaurus
2. The tooth indicated that duck-billed dinosaurs were plant eaters. They could not have survived without plants to eat.
3. Coal forms from fossilized plants, and coal beds were found in Antarctica; two species of tree fern fossils were found; tree stem, root, and pollen fossils have been found; and British geologists have fossil evidence that great ancient forests in Antarctica match forests that grew on the Pacific Coast of the Unites States 20 million years ago.
4. Antarctica was warm. Labyrinthodonts, whose fossils were found in Antarctica, could not have survived in a cold climate. Most plants cannot grow in a climate like the one Antarctica has today, either.
5. Analysis of mountain rocks showed signs that sediments were carried into the area.
6. Scientists believe Antarctica was located close to Australia and South America. Similar fossils, such as those of the duck-billed dinosaur, found on these continents indicate that the animals could move easily between these places.
7. Your student should draw a scene that shows vegetation, flowing water, and a version of a duck-billed dinosaur.

ASSESS

Lesson Assessment: Fossils (*Offline*)

Students will complete an offline assessment based on the lesson objectives. Print the assessment and have students complete it on their own. Use the answer key to score the assessment, and then enter the results online. The attached answer key is the most current and may not coincide with previously printed guides.

Fossils Lesson Assessment Answer Key

Short Answer

Answer each question in the space provided.

1. Give an example of a body fossil.

   Answers may vary. Acceptable answers should refer to the shape and structure of an
   organism, such as bones, shells, or leaf imprints.

2. Give an example of a trace fossil.

   Answers may vary. Acceptable answers should refer to the movement or behavior of an
   organism, such as footprints.

3. Why would a leaf be preserved only as an impression?

   The leaf is soft and will decay before forming a fossil. Its impression will be left in the dried
   mud where it fell. This mud may eventually turn into rock.

4. Study the diagram below. What do the two types of fossils found in these two rock layers tell
   you about the changes in the environment in this area over time?

   The shell fossil means that the area was once covered by water. The lizard fossil means that
   the area changed and contained dry land.

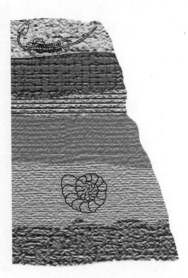

Learning Coach Guide
Lesson 5: Records in Rocks

Your student will learn basic principles of how fossils are laid down in sedimentary rock. Building on these principles, your student will learn how geologists determine the age of a fossil, and the rock in which it is embedded.

Lesson Objectives

- Explain how scientists use rock layers to gain information about earth's geologic past.

PREPARE

Approximate lesson time is 60 minutes.

Materials

For the Student
- Rock Record

For the Adult
- Rock Record Answer Key

Keywords and Pronunciation

brachiopod (BRAY-kee-uh-pahd)

unconformity (uhn-kuhn-FAWR-muh-tee) : a gap in the rock record that indicated a time where *no* deposition has occurred, or where erosion *has* taken place

---

TEACH
Activity 1: Rock Layers Revealed *(Online)*

Instructions

Your student will understand that fossils provide evidence of past life. Three principles for understanding relationships between sedimentary rocks will be explained and applied to the Grand Canyon.

Activity 2: Rock Record *(Offline)*

Instructions

Information about earth's history can be found in layers of sedimentary rock. Reading a rock record displaying multiple layers of sedimentary rock provides clues to geologic events such as folding, faulting, tilting, or erosion. Your student will read two sample rock records and then make inferences about folding, tilting, erosion, and unconformities using Steno's principles.

ASSESS

Lesson Assessment: Records in Rocks, Part 1 (*Online*)

Students will complete an online assessment based on the lesson objectives. The assessment will be scored by the computer. The attached answer key is the most current and may not coincide with previously printed guides.

Lesson Assessment: Records in Rocks, Part 2 (*Offline*)

Students will complete an offline assessment based on the lesson objectives. Print the assessment and have students complete it on their own. Use the answer key to score the assessment, and then enter the results online. The attached answer key is the most current and may not coincide with previously printed guides.

Name _____   Date _____

Rock Record Answer Key

Record A.

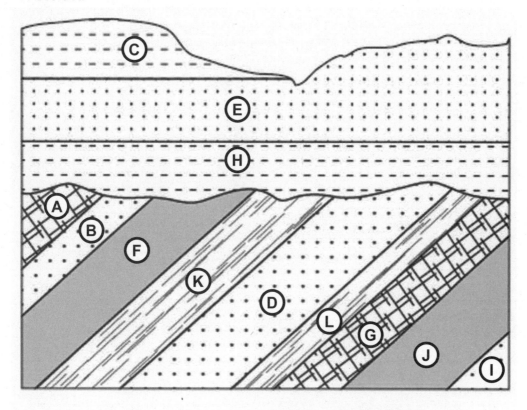

Record B.

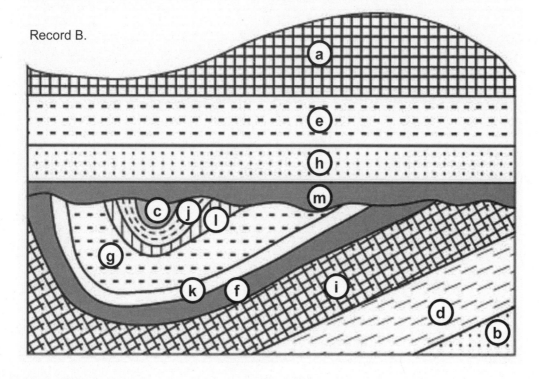

Name   Date

Use the Rock Record on page 1 to complete the questions below.

1. Examine Record A. Use the three basic rules to figure out the ages of the layers. In Chart A, list the layers from youngest to oldest, with the youngest layer in the first row.

2. Look for signs of tilting, erosion, or folding. In the second column in Chart A, write whether you think tilting, erosion, or folding took place. Write "tilting," "erosion," or "folding" next to the letter of any rock layer that was formed when the tilting, erosion, or folding took place. If you see no evidence of tilting, erosion, or folding, write "none."

3. Repeat steps 1 and 2 for Record B. Record the data in Chart B.

Data

Chart A	
Rock Layers (youngest to oldest)	**Tilting, Erosion, or Folding**
1 C	Erosion
2 E	Erosion
3 H	None
4 A	Tilting
5 B	Tilting
6 F	Tilting
7 K	Tilting
8 D	Tilting
9 L	Tilting
10 G	Tilting
11 J	Tilting
12 I	Tilting

Name _____   Date _____

Chart B	
Rock Layers (youngest to oldest)	**Tilting, Erosion, or Folding**
1 a	Erosion
2 e	None
3 h	None
4 m	None
5 c	Folding
6 j	Folding
7 l	Folding
8 g	Folding
9 k	Folding
10 f	Folding
11 i	Folding
12 d	Tilting
13 b	Tilting

Observations

1. Where does the unconformity occur in Record A and Record B?

    Record A – before layer *H*, Record B – before layer *m*

Name _____   Date _____

Analysis

2. Study Record A. What can you say about the age of layer *K* from your data
    and observations?

    K is an older layer of rock. It is still younger than *I, J, G, L,* and *D*. _____

3. Study Record B. What can you say about the age of layer *c* from your data
    and observations?

    Layer *c* is younger than j, older than m and folded. _____

4. What do you think took place in layers C and E, exposed at the top surface of the layers in
    record A?

    They are exposed at the top because of erosion. _____

Conclusions

5. Write about how the group of rock layers in Record A formed. Include tilting, erosion,
    and folding.

    Rock layers *I, J, G, L, D, K, F, B,* and *A* are all very old layers of rock (from oldest to youngest).

    Due to folding, all of these layers are tilting. Layers *H, E,* and *C* are all newer layers of rocks.

    Layers *E* and *C* have experienced erosion because they are exposed on the surface of

    the earth.

6.   Write about how the group of rock layers in Record B formed. Include tilting, erosion,
    and folding.

    Rock layers *b* and *d* are very old layers of rocks, both of which are tilting. Between layers

    d and *i* more folding occurred, causing the layers to fold. These tilted layers, caused from

    folding, include *k, f, g, l, j,* and *c*. The newer layers of rock of *h, e,* and *a* were then layered over

    layer *m*. Layer *a* is experiencing erosion because it is exposed to the surface.

Name _____ Date _____

Record in Rocks, Part 2 Lesson Assessment Answer Key

Use the diagram below to answer questions 1, 2, and 3.

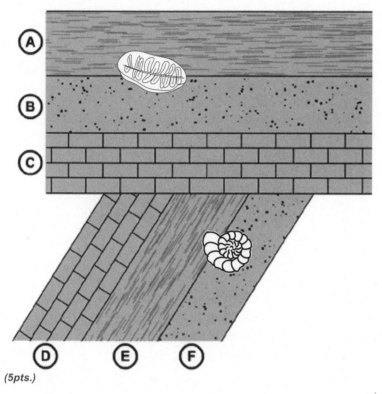

(5pts.)

1. There is evidence of an unconformity between which two layers?

   between layers *C* and *D*

(10 pts.)

2. In searching rock layers for fossils, you make an interesting discovery. In layer F, you find fossilized clam shells. In layer B, you find fossilized leaf and tree impressions. What would you say about the environment where these layers were deposited?

   Answers may vary but should include: Layer F was most likely a marine environment. Layer B was most likely a forest environment.

(10 pts.)

3. Which existed first, the clam or the leaf? Why?

   Answers may vary but should include: The clam. It is found in a lower layer than the leaf fossil, and so it was deposited first.

Learning Coach Guide
Lesson 6: Lab: Index Fossils and Paleoenvironments

One of the continuing aspects of geology is locating and describing new fossils. These fossils not only tell about life in the past, but they can also be used to understand the rock layers in which they were found. Your student will use fossils to match rock layers in two different places on earth and then find out what clues fossils provide to understanding environments of the past.

Lesson Objectives

- Investigate how fossil patterns in rock layers provide information about earth's geologic past.

PREPARE

Approximate lesson time is 60 minutes.

Materials

For the Student

🖳 Rock Layers and Index Fossils

pencils, colored 12

For the Adult

🖳 Rock Layers and Index Fossils Answer Key

Keywords and Pronunciation

index fossil : a fossil found to be especially useful in correlating rock layers across large distances

paleobotany (PAY-lee-oh-BAH-tuh-nee)

paleoenvironment (PAY-lee-oh-in-VIH-ruhn-muhnt)

strata : stratum (plural, strata): a single sedimentary rock unit with a distinct set of mineralogical characteristics or fossils that allow the layer to be easily distinguished from the rocky layers above and below it

---

TEACH
Activity 1: Pre-Lab: Index Fossils (Online)

Instructions

Index fossils can be used to correlate or match rock layers separated by large distances. They are fossils paleontologists have found to be especially useful in correlating rock layers across large distances. Index fossils can also provide information about the types of environments in which they lived. Your student will learn how index fossils provide valuable clues to geologists and paleontologists who are interested in reconstructing earth's history.

Activity 2: Index Fossils and Paleoenvironments *(Offline)*
Instructions
In this activity, your student will practice stratigraphy by using a fossil to correlate rock layers found in Idaho and Spain.

ASSESS
Lesson Assessment: Lab: Index Fossils and Paleoenvironments (*Online*)
Review your student's responses on the Index Fossils and Paleoenvironments Lab and input the results online. The attached answer key is the most current and may not coincide with previously printed guides.

Name _____   Date _____

Rock Layers Revealed Answer Key

Figure 1: Rock Layers

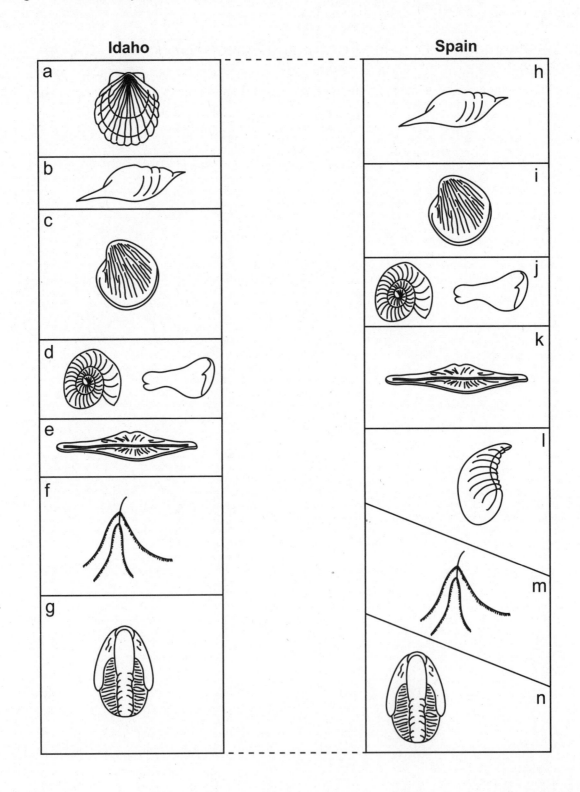

Name _____   Date _____

Answer to Analysis

layer j _____

Answers to Conclusion

1. Your student should state whether his hypothesis matched the answers. Clues may be related to the information about other fossil evidence found in the rock layers.

2. Key answer features: The information about fossils found in these two layers could be used to match new layers in a new location.

3. Answers will vary. Key answer features: Relative dating is useful in determining the order in which earth's history unfolded. It provides a big picture view of the development of life and landforms on earth.

Name _____   Date _____

Lab: Index Fossils and Paleoenvironments Lesson Assessment Answer Key

Answers:

1. Review your student's responses in the Rock Layers Revealed activity sheet to determine if the proceedures outlined in the Student Guide were followed in order to gather all pertinent data from the experiment.

2. Refer to the **Analysis** section of the Student Guide: layer j.

3. Refer to the **Conclusion** section of the Student Guide. Answers may vary but should include: The information about fossils found in these two layers could be used to match new layers in a new location.

Learning Coach Guide
Lesson 7: A Journey Through Geologic Time

This lesson demonstrates how periods of earth's history can be grouped into segments of time. Your student will explore the geologic timeline by identifying climate, life on earth, and geologic activity in various periods of earth's development.

Lesson Objectives

- Interpret a diagram of geologic time scale, including eons, eras, periods, and the approximate time frame for these events.

PREPARE

Approximate lesson time is 60 minutes.

Advance Preparation

- This lesson presents information consistent with the general scientific consensus about the age of the earth.

Materials

For the Student

    📖 Exploring Geologic Time

    📖 Geologic Time in a Year

For the Adult

    📖 Geologic Time in a Year Answer Key

Keywords and Pronunciation

Cambrian (KAM-bree-uhn)

Carboniferous (KAHR-buh-NIH-fuh-ruhs)

Cenozoic (see-nuh-ZOH-ihk)

Cretaceous (kree-TAY-shuhs)

Devonian (dih-VO-nee-uhn)

eon (EE-ahn) : the longest period of geologic time

epoch (EH-puhk) : a subdivision of a period in geologic time

era : the longest unit of time on the geologic time scale (Do not confuse it with the word *eon*, which is a term indicating time longer than an era.)

extinction : the dying out of a species so that no members exist

Jurassic (juh-RA-sihk)

Mesozoic (meh-zuh-ZOH-ihk)

Ordovician (OR-duh-VI-shuhn)

Paleozoic (pay-lee-uh-ZOH-ihk)

period : a subdivision of an era in geological time

Permian (PUHR-mee-uhn)

Precambrian (pree-KAM-bree-uhn)
Quaternary (kwuh-TUHR-nair-ee)
Silurian (sih-LOUR-ee-uhn)
Tertiary (TUHR-shi-air-ee)
Triassic (triy-A-sihk)

TEACH
Activity 1: Understanding Geologic Time *(Online)*
Instructions

The divisions of geologic time will be explained with references to geologic events, life on earth including major extinctions, and climate.

Answers to Exploring Geologic Time Activity

1. Phanerozoic
2. Extinction
3. Mesozoic
4. Carboniferous
5. Three
6. Appalachian
7. Oxygen
8. Columbia
9. Cenozoic

Chicxulub Crater

Think About It: More plant and animal life develops and flourishes in warm climates than in cold. Answer should include: The Cryogenian period was very cold; earth suffered its most extreme ice age in history. At this time, there was little plant and animal life developing on earth. The Eocene was very warm and primates developed along with grasses. Palm trees grew in Alaska. The Cretaceous Period was also very warm and life such as flowering plants, small mammals, and dinosaurs were present on earth.

Activity 2: Geologic Time in a Year *(Offline)*
Instructions

In this activity, your student will attempt to compress events of geologic time into one calendar year. This model helps with understanding the length of geologic time, including how recently human development occurred.

You can approach the activity several ways.

- Visit the University of Kentucky Geologic Time Line and copy the answers. They used a slightly different math formula so our answer key differs from their timeline. You can still focus on the point of the activity which makes geologic time more concrete by compressing millions of years into months and days.

- Estimate the dates using the data already in the table.
- Use a mathematical formula. Here's how:

First small dinosaurs

1. Subtract the year in the left column from the age of the earth, 4.6 billion years.

4,600,000,000 years - 228,000,000 years = 4,372,000,000 years

2. Divide by the number of years in a day.

4,372,000,000 years / 12602740 years in a day = 346 days (don't round)

3. Divide the days by 31 (days in a month)

346 days / 31 days in a month = 11.19 months

4. Now we know that at least 11 months have gone by, so the event happened in December. But which day? We need to find out how many days 0.19 months is.

0.19 month x 31 days in a month = 5.89 Don't round!

4. We know that at least 5 days have gone by so we are on day 6.

5. The numbers after the decimal can give you a clue as to what time of DAY the event happened. If it's less than 0.5, it happened before noon. Multiply the two numbers after the decimal by 24 to find the hour.

0.89 day x 24 hours in a day = 21.36 hours or 9 PM

6. Find the minutes by multiplying the digits after the decimal by 60.

0.36 hours X 60 minutes in an hour =21.6

The event happened December 6 at 9:26 PM

You might be thinking your calculator doesn't have enough spaces for 4.6 billion years. Your computer should have a calculator that can hold large numbers like these.

ASSESS

Lesson Assessment: A Journey Through Geologic Time, Part 1 (*Online*)

Students will complete an online assessment based on the lesson objectives. The assessment will be scored by the computer. The attached answer key is the most current and may not coincide with previously printed guides.

Lesson Assessment: A Journey Through Geologic Time, Part 2 (*Offline*)

Students will complete an offline assessment based on the lesson objectives. Print the assessment and have students complete it on their own. Use the answer key to score the assessment, and then enter the results online. The attached answer key is the most current and may not coincide with previously printed guides.

Name   Date

Geologic Time in a Year Answer Key

Directions

Below are some events in earth's history. Imagine that geologic time is compressed to the space of one calendar year. At this scale, 1 day equals about 12,602,740 years! When would the events below occur if we could compress geologic time in this way? There are a few hints to help you. You should guess the date but do not have to guess the exact time. Some of the data for this activity has been provided by the Kentucky Geological Survey, a research center of the University of Kentucky.

Years ago	Time	Event	Date if time was compressed to a calendar year
4.6 bya	Precambrian	Beginning of earth	1/1/00 12:00 AM
3.8 bya	Precambrian	Oldest age-dated rocks on earth	3/5/00 11:28 AM
1.5 bya	Ectasian Period	First multicelled organisms (seaweed and algae)	09/3/00 11:28 PM
505 mya	Cambrian Period	First fish	11/21/00 10:18 PM
470 mya	Silurian Period	First fossil evidence of land plants	11/24/00 4:57 PM
385 mya	Devonian Period	First insects (beetles, scorpions, centipedes)	12/1/00 10:49 AM
375 mya	Devonian Period	First land animals	12/2/00 5:52 AM
370 mya	Devonian Period	First sharks	12/2/00 3:23 PM
365 mya	Carboniferous Period	First seed plants	12/3/00 12:54 AM
228 mya	Triassic Period	First small dinosaurs	12/13/00 9:48 PM
115 mya	Cretaceous period	First flowering plants	12/22/00 9:00 PM
70 mya	Cretaceous Period	Tyrannosaurus Rex and Velociraptor	12/26/00 10:41 AM
64 mya	Paleocene Epoch	First ancestors of dogs and cats	12/26/00 10:07 PM
55 mya	Eocene Epoch	First horses	12/27/00 3:15 PM
39 mya	Eocene Epoch	First monkeys	12/28/00 9:43 PM
4 mya	Pliocene	First human-like ancestors	12/31/00 5:20 PM
0.1 mya	Recent Epoch	First modern man	12/31/00 11:48 PM

Name _____   Date _____

A Journey Through Geologic Time Lesson Assessment Answer Key

Directions

Read the question carefully and answer on the lines provided.

(10 pts)

1. Geologic time is divided into segments based on two kinds of information. What are they?

   The appearance and disappearance of fossils , and major physical changes on the

   earth's surface.

   _____

(9 pts.)

2. Describe the climate, landforms, and existing plant and animal life during the Cretaceous Period.

   Earth's climate was warm and tropical with no ice at the poles. Life on earth included plants

   such as flowering plants, small mammals, insects, and dinosaurs. The Rocky Mountains

   began to form during this period.

Learning Coach Guide
Lesson 8: Geologic History Unit Review

In this lesson, your student will prepare for the unit assessment. He will complete review questions online, and then review concepts from the unit while learning about the La Brea Tar Pits in Los Angeles, California. Rancho La Brea is a hotbed of fossil discovery from the Pleistocene epoch over 10,000 years ago.

Lesson Objectives

- Recognize the principle of uniformitarianism and its importance in determining historical events based on geological information.
- Recognize how fossils can be interpreted as evidence of preexisting life.
- Recognize and explain methods by which scientists determine the sequence of geological events, and the life forms and environmental conditions that existed in past geologic eras.
- Describe the geologic time scale and provide examples of major geological and biological events of each era.
- Recognize the major historic contributions to interpreting sedimentary rock layers made by James Hutton and Charles Lyell.

PREPARE

Approximate lesson time is 60 minutes.

Materials

For the Student

💻 Geologic Map of California

TEACH
Activity 1: Prepare for the La Brea Tar Pits *(Online)*
Instructions
Your student will complete a short, online review of concepts learned in this unit.

Activity 2: A Visit to Rancho La Brea *(Online)*
Instructions
Answers to Unit Review

1. Cenozoic, Quaternary, Pleistocene
2. Woolly mammoths, saber-toothed cats, mastodons, possibly horses, camels, and cheetahs.
3. Your student should label the area between the Transverse Ranges and the San Gabriel Fault in southern California.
4. Precambrian (or Paleozoic with Precambrian metamorphic rocks)
5. Absolute dating

---

6. The rock around Rancho La Brea is better for finding fossils because it is sedimentary rock. Fossils form in sedimentary rock as new layers of rock form over them. The Sierra Nevada mountains are made from igneous rock.

7. Saber-toothed cats were land animals. Rock in the Coastal Ranges would most likely contain fossils of animals that lived in water.

8. Body fossils

9. Trace fossils

10. Dinosaurs went extinct 65 million years ago; the fossils found at La Brea are more recent, ranging from 10,000 to 40,000 years ago.

11. Rancho La Brea's climate was wetter.

12. Rancho La Brea's climate now is and drier.

Learning Coach Guide
Lesson 9: Geologic History Unit Assessment

Your student will take the Geologic History Unit Assessment.

Lesson Objectives

- Recognize the principle of uniformitarianism and its importance in determining historical events based on geological information.
- Recognize how fossils can be interpreted as evidence of preexisting life.
- Recognize and explain methods by which scientists determine the sequence of geological events, and the life forms and environmental conditions that existed in past geologic eras.
- Describe the geologic time scale and provide examples of major geological and biological events of each era.
- Recognize the major historic contributions to interpreting sedimentary rock layers made by James Hutton and Charles Lyell.

PREPARE

Approximate lesson time is 60 minutes.

ASSESS

Unit Assessment: Geologic History Unit Assessment, Part 1 (*Online*)

Students will complete an online assessment of the objectives covered so far in this unit. The assessment will be scored by the computer. The attached answer key is the most current and may not coincide with previously printed guides.

Unit Assessment: Geologic History Unit Assessment, Part 2 (*Offline*)

Students will complete an offline Unit Assessment. Print the assessment and have students complete it on their own. Use the answer key to score the assessment, and then enter the results online. The attached answer key is the most current and may not coincide with previously printed guides.

Learning Coach Guide
Lesson 1. Optional: Your Choice

Lesson Objectives

- Practice skills and reinforce concepts taught in this course.

PREPARE

Approximate lesson time is 60 minutes.

Learning Coach Guide
Lesson 2: The Center of the Earth

Lesson Objectives

- Interpret a diagram that depicts the structure of the earth's interior.
- Compare temperature, pressure, and composition of earth's inner and outer cores.

PREPARE

Approximate lesson time is 60 minutes.

Advance Preparation

- You will need an unpeeled, hard-boiled egg for this lesson.

Materials

For the Student

📖 Earth as an Egg

eggs, hard-boiled

knife, plastic

napkin

plate

For the Adult

📖 Earth as an Egg Answer Key

Keywords and Pronunciation

asthenosphere (as-THE-nuh-sfir) : the upper part of the earth´s mantle

cross section : a section formed by a plane cutting through an object

crust : the outermost, solid layer of any planet or moon

exterior : the outer surface or part

interior : the inside of anything

lithosphere (LIH-the-sfir) : the rocky outer layer of the solid earth, averaging about 100 km in depth; the lithosphere includes the continents, islands, and the entire ocean floor

mantle : the part of earth that is beneath the crust and is made up of rock; about 84 percent of the earth´s volume is in the mantle

molten : made liquid by heat, melted

plasticity (pla-STIS-i-tee) : capable of being molded

TEACH
Activity 1: A Look at the Earth's Layers (Online)
Instructions
Your student will explore the earth's interior layers, including the crust, mantle, and the inner and outer cores.

Activity 2: Earth as an Egg (Offline)
Instructions
Your student will use an egg to label and describe the features of the earth's layers, including physical features, depth, and composition.
Safety
Use the knife with caution and with adult supervision.

Activity 3: The Center of the Earth (Offline)
Instructions
In this activity, your student will review the concepts learned in this lesson. Store the review sheet in your student's Science Notebook.

Answers
1. outer core
2. oceanic crust
3. inner core
4. mantle
5. crust
6. lithosphere
7. mantle (or asthenosphere)

ASSESS

Lesson Assessment: The Center of the Earth (Online)
Students will complete an online assessment based on the lesson objectives. The assessment will be scored by the computer. The attached answer key is the most current and may not coincide with previously printed guides.

Name _____   Date _____

Earth as an Egg Answer Key

Using an egg as a model, you can learn about the structure of the earth's interior.

Materials:

egg, hard-boiled
plate
napkin
plastic knife

Procedure:

1. Study the exterior of the egg.

2. Tap the egg lightly on all sides until the shell shows a few cracks.

3. Press lightly on the egg to move the cracked shell. Try to make a few pieces of shell collide into one another.

4. Press a piece of the cracked shell into the second layer of the egg, forcing pieces of egg to the top.

5. Cut the egg in half. Study the cross-section.

Observations:

1. What part of the earth did the eggshell represent?

   the crust _____

2. What layer of "earth" showed through when you cracked the shell?

   the mantle _____

3. What layer of "earth" did the yolk represent?

   the core _____

4. Think about it: Which action could have demonstrated an earthquake?

   moving the pieces of cracked shell toward and away from each other _____

5. Think about it: Which action demonstrated an eruption of lava as through a volcano?

   pushing the pieces of shell into the egg _____

Study the diagram below. Label each layer of the earth.

inner core

outer core

mantle

crust

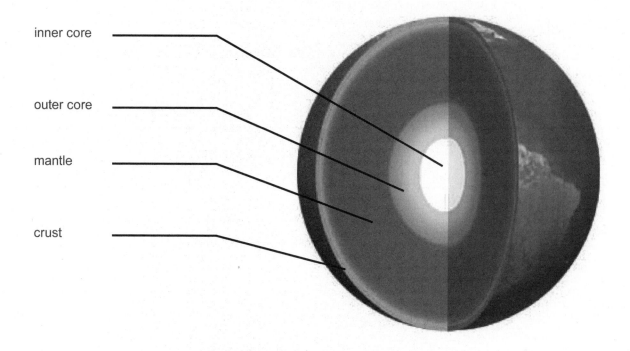

Learning Coach Guide
Lesson 3: Continental Drift

The theory of plate tectonics incorporated and explained many of the main ideas in the theory of continental drift. That theory itself was revolutionary in hypothesizing that whole continents had moved around the surface of the earth. Your student will explore the theory of continental drift, including the movement of the continents and the evidence scientists have gathered related to this theory.

Lesson Objectives

- Summarize continental drift as an example of a scientific theory that changed in response to new evidence.
- Define and explain Pangaea.

PREPARE

Approximate lesson time is 60 minutes.

Materials

For the Student

    📖 Continents Map

    📖 Investigating a Supercontinent

    highlighter

    construction paper

    glue or tape

    scissors

For the Adult

    📖 Investigating a Supercontinent Answer Key

Keywords and Pronunciation

Theory of Continental Drift : the theory that the continents were previously joined together, and over time broke up and slowly drifted apart to their present positions

Abraham Ortelius (AY-bruh-ham or-TEL-ee-uhs)

Alfred Wegener (AHL-frayt VAY-guh-nuhr)

continental drift : the slow movement of continental plates over earth's surface

Gondwanaland (gawn-DWAH-nuh-land)

Laurasia (law-RAY-zhuh)

mesosaurus (meh-soh-SAWR-uhs)

Pangaea (pan-JEE-uh) : the name scientists give to a supercontinent that once existed on earth

TEACH
Activity 1: A New Theory (Online)
Instructions
In this activity your student will learn how the theory of continental drift developed and about evidence that supported that theory.

Activity 2: Investigating a Supercontinent (Offline)
Instructions
Your student will arrange the continents to get a glimpse of the past and explore how Alfred Wegener theorized that all of the continents were once joined together in a supercontinent called Pangaea.

Activity 3: Continental Drift (Offline)
Instructions
In this activity, your student will review the concepts learned in this lesson. Store the review sheet in your student's Science Notebook.

Answers
1. continents
2. Abraham Ortelius
3. Alfred Wegener
4. continental drift
5. fossils
6. mesosaurs
7. Pangaea
8. Laurasia
9. Gondwanaland

ASSESS

Lesson Assessment: Continental Drift, Part 1 (Online)
Students will complete an online assessment based on the lesson objectives. The assessment will be scored by the computer. The attached answer key is the most current and may not coincide with previously printed guides.

Lesson Assessment: Continental Drift, Part 2 (Offline)
Students will complete an offline assessment based on the lesson objectives. Print the assessment and have students complete it on their own. Use the answer key to score the assessment, and then enter the results online. The attached answer key is the most current and may not coincide with previously printed guides.

Name _____ Date _____

Investigating a Supercontinent Answer Key

Shapes of Coastlines

1. Use your world map to study the edges of Africa and South America. Describe the match between them.

   The eastern side of South America fits into the southwestern side of Africa.

2. Cut the continents from the Continent Map. Try to arrange them on construction paper as one large landmass according to their shapes, but do not glue them yet. Notice the locations of any overlapping areas.

Mountain Ranges

Many mountain ranges that today appear on one continent are similar in age and form to mountain ranges on another continent. Some of these mountain ranges are shown on your continent cutouts. They are numbered according to those ranges that are similar to one another.

3. Check the landmass you created to see if the common mountain ranges line up with one another. Make any changes in your model now that you know about the mountain ranges.

Fossils

Several fossils are found on certain landmasses but not on others. Look at each landmass. Using the key, notice which fossils were found on each landmass.

4. Which fossils were found in both Africa and South America?

   cynognathus, mesosaurus, and glossopteris

5. Adjust your model based on the fossil information.

Glacier Evidence

The map below shows where evidence of ice sheets 300 million years old has been found in the Southern Hemisphere. The dashed line on the map connects all the places where plowed rock and sediment have been found on the continents. The arrows show the direction of glacier movement.

Name _____   Date _____

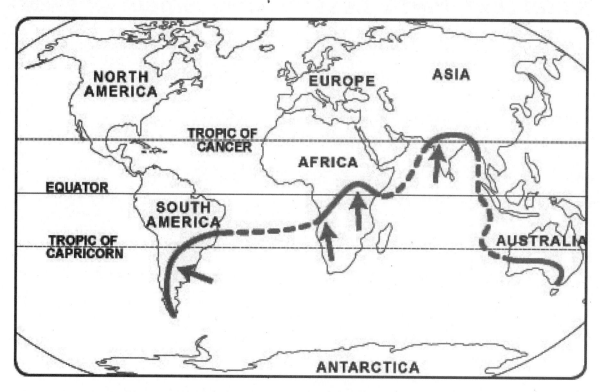

6.   Use a highlighter to draw the information about glaciers onto the landmasses you have been arranging on the construction paper.

7.   Make any changes in your model now that you know about glacial evidence.

When you are satisfied with the model you've created, glue your landmasses to the construction paper, and then answer the questions below.

Questions

8.   What kinds of evidence can be used to show that a supercontinent once existed?

The coastlines of continents, fossil remains, mountain formation, and glacier movement are kinds of evidence that can be used to show that a supercontinent existed.

9.   In your own words, explain the theory of continental drift.

Answers will vary but should include key words such as: fossil evidence, mountain range evidence, Pangaea, and shapes of coastlines.

10.   Why do you think it took so long for scientists to accept the idea of continental drift?

Answers will vary but may include that it takes millions of years to find evidence, such as fossils and evidence of glacial movement.

11.   What other evidence would you like to have to prove that the earth's surface has moved and is moving? What other questions would you like answered and explained?

Answers will vary.

Name _____   Date _____

Continental Drift, Part 2 Lesson Assessment Answer Key

Read each question carefully, and then write the answer on the lines provided.

10 pts.

1. Explain how mountain chains provide evidence to support the theory of continental drift.

Mountain chains that are now separated by bodies of water on different continents would match up if these continents are placed next to each other, as they were when Pangaea existed.

10 pts.

2. What is one reason why many geologists did not at first accept the theory of continental drift?

No one could provide a good explanation for how huge continents could have moved across the earth's surface. Scientists also held on to older ideas that made sense.

Learning Coach Guide
Lesson 4: Seafloor Geography

During the last 50 years of detailed seafloor mapping, scientists have discovered important information about the ocean floor. Studies revealed that the ocean floor is not featureless and is dynamic. It provides evidence explaining how continents can move throughout long periods of time. Your student will try an early method of seafloor mapping using weighted lines.

Lesson Objectives

- Identify features of the ocean floor.
- Explain how ocean floor mapping led to information that advanced the theory of continental drift.

PREPARE

Approximate lesson time is 60 minutes.

Advance Preparation

- This lesson presents information consistent with the general scientific consensus about the age of the earth.

Materials

For the Student

📇 Activity Instructions

📇 Graph Paper

books (3)

meter stick

tissue box

chairs (2)

markers or crayons

ruler

scissors

string - about 3 meters

trash can - small

washer, metal

Keywords and Pronunciation

abyssal plain : a flat expanse of ocean floor

bathymetric (ba-thih-MEH-trihk) : a type of data collected from measurement of the depths of oceans, seas, or other large bodies of water

continental rise : a region of gentle slope between the continental slope and the main ocean floor

continental shelf : a shelf of undersea land reaching a depth of about 200 meters (656 feet), extending out from the shoreline

continental slope : the relatively steeply sloping undersea land extending from the outer edge of the continental shelf

guyot (GEE-oh) : a seamount with a flattened top

midocean ridge : a long, raised area in the ocean, with a depression or valley running along its top

seamount : a volcanic mountain that rises from the ocean floor and has its peak underwater

submarine canyon : a deep channel on the ocean floor, in the outer continental shelf, in the continental slope, or in the continental rise

TEACH
Activity 1: Under the Sea *(Online)*
Instructions
At the bottom of the ocean lie features larger and longer than some we see on land. Your student will explore these features as well as the methods used for mapping them. The evidence for seafloor spreading will be explained.

Activity 2: Mapping the Ocean Floor *(Offline)*
Instructions
Early maps of the seafloor were made using weighted lines dropped to the bottom of the floor. Your student will simulate this method of mapping the ocean floor with a weighted string and household objects.

Answers:
1. The map made at 5 cm intervals most closely resembles the ocean floor. When measuring at smaller intervals, more details about the ocean floor are detected and are more accurately represented than when measuring at larger intervals.
2. Sonar is more accurate than weighted lines to map the ocean floor for several reasons. It is possible to use sonar at closely spaced locations on the ocean floor, whereas weighted lines are dropped only at wider intervals to collect data. With sonar, the measuring points can be very close together. Sonar is also faster and more reliable in direction. If the ship or line drifts in the water, the line will not be vertical. This would result in a measurement longer than the actual depth between the ship and the ocean bottom, to a point not directly beneath the ship.

ASSESS
Lesson Assessment: Seafloor Geography (*Online*)
Students will complete an offline assessment based on the lesson objectives. Print the assessment and have students complete it on their own. Use the answer key to score the assessment, and then enter the results online. The attached answer key is the most current and may not coincide with previously printed guides.

Name   Date

Seafloor Geography Lesson Assessment Answer Key

(10 pts.)

1. Fill in each blank with a term from the Word Bank. You will use each term only once, and you will use all of the terms.

Word Bank

> continental shelf   guyot   deep-sea trench
>
>   seamount
> continental rise   abyssal plain
>   continental slope

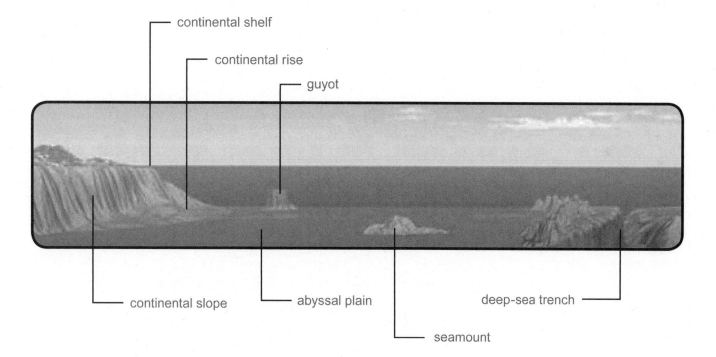

(10 pts.)

2. Mapping the seafloor resulted in two pieces of information that made the theory of continental drift sound more likely. What were they?

    The discovery that the ocean floor had landforms and geologic processes showed that it was

    linked to geologic processes on land. Also, sediment was found that was thinner than it should

    have been if the ocean floor had always been in the same place.

Learning Coach Guide
Lesson 5: Seafloor Spreading

Lesson Objectives
- Explain how magnetism in rocks was used as evidence to support the concept of seafloor spreading.
- Describe how seafloor spreading results in the formation of new crust.

PREPARE

Approximate lesson time is 60 minutes.

Materials
For the Student

⊟ What's the Spread?

calculator

ruler

For the Adult

⊟ What's the Spread? Answer Key

Keywords and Pronunciation
paleomagnetism (pay-lee-oh-MAG-nuh-tih-zuhm) : magnetic qualities "frozen" into rocks when they are formed, including the direction of the magnetic field

TEACH
Activity 1: Magnetism and the Seafloor (Online)

Activity 2: What's the Spread? (Offline)
Instructions
Students will use measurements and time to calculate the rate and amount of seafloor spreading that has occurred in the Mid-Atlantic Ridge. This activity may be challenging so encourage your student to follow directions closely. Spreading rates at the Mid-Atlantic Ridge vary all along the ridge so the answer key provides a range of target answers for your student.

You may want to extend the activity with a discussion of seafloor spreading. Students who grasp the concept will understand that if seafloor is created at mid-ocean ridges, it must be destroyed somewhere else. Otherwise, earth would be expanding. This will be explored in the next lesson.

ASSESS

Lesson Assessment: Seafloor Spreading, Part 1 (*Online*)

Students will complete an online assessment based on the lesson objectives. The assessment will be scored by the computer. The attached answer key is the most current and may not coincide with previously printed guides.

Lesson Assessment: Seafloor Spreading, Part 2 (*Offline*)

Students will complete an offline assessment based on the lesson objectives. Print the assessment and have students complete it on their own. Use the answer key to score the assessment, and then enter the results online. The attached answer key is the most current and may not coincide with previously printed guides.

Name _____   Date _____

What's the Spread? Answer Key

Each year, new seafloor is added at the Mid-Atlantic Ridge. The Atlantic Ocean widens causing North and South America to move farther away from Europe and Africa. Close to the ridge, rocks are younger. As you move away from the ridge, the rocks become older.

1. Where would you find the oldest sections of seafloor, near the continents or near the Mid-Atlantic Ridge?

   near the continents

The rate of seafloor spreading has not been the same over time. In this activity, you will calculate the average rate of seafloor spreading, and then determine when the seafloor started to spread.

Materials

Ruler
Calculator
Geologic Timeline in Unit Resources

Procedure

Working with Map Scales

Below is a map of a section of the North Atlantic. You can see the coastlines of North America and Africa. On both sides of the Mid-Atlantic Ridge strips of seafloor are labeled with their ages in millions of years. Note the map scale.

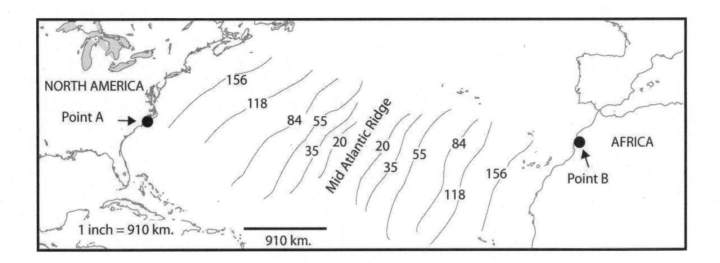

1. What is the scale of the map? For this activity, you will use inches.

   1 in = 910 km

2. Choose one strip of seafloor rock. Write the age of the rock here:_____million years

3. Use your ruler to measure the distance of the strip from the Mid-Atlantic Ridge. _____ inches

4. Using the calculator, divide the answer to #3 by 910 to figure out its distance in kilometers. _____ km.

Determining Rate of Spreading

Use the age of the rock you have chosen and its distance from the Mid-Atlantic Ridge to calculate seafloor spreading.

5. First you will find out how fast the seafloor is moving away from the ridge on one side. Use the calculator to divide the answer to #4 by the answer to #2.

   #4 _____ km ÷ #2 _____ million years = Answer will vary between 9 and 12 km /1 million years

6. Now find out how fast the seafloor widens every 1 million years. Multiply the answer you got in #5 by 2. The seafloor spreads at a rate of Answer will vary between 18 and 24 km every 1 million years.

When Did the Seafloor Start Spreading?

The distance between Point A and Point B, or the coasts of Africa and North America, is 4,550 km. Using your answer to #6, find out when the Atlantic Ocean began to open. Divide your answer in # 6 by 4,550 km to find out.

7. #6 _____ ÷ 4,550 = Answer will vary between 190–230 million years ago.

8. Look at the Geologic Timeline. During what geologic period did the Atlantic start to open?
   the late Triassic or early Jurassic periods

Challenge

See if you can figure out how much the distance between North America and Africa has increased since you were born.

9. #6 _____ x 0.62 x 5,280 x 12 x 0.000001 = Answer will vary around 0.78 inches/year

10. How far, in inches, has the distance between North America and Africa increased since you were born?
    Answer will vary around 8 inches

11. How much does the distance increase during the average lifetime of 82 years?
    Answer will vary around 64 inches

Super Challenge

12. How much closer were the continents when Columbus crossed the Atlantic in 1492?
    Answer will vary around 400 inches

Name _____   Date _____

Seafloor Spreading, Part 2 Lesson Assessment Answer Key

Read and answer the questions below.

10 pts.

1. Explain how seafloor spreading results in new oceanic crust. You may include a drawing in your explanation.

The seafloor spreads out, creating an opening in the crust. Magma from beneath the surface moves upward, into the opening at the mid-ocean ridge formed by this spreading. There, magma cools and solidifies to form new seafloor.

10 pts.

2. Explain how a prediction and then evidence of magnetism in rocks on the ocean floor proved that the seafloor spreads.

In new, liquid rock, magnetic mineral grains line up with earth's magnetic field. When the rocks cool and become solid, these magnetic mineral grains remain locked in place. Over time, the ocean floor records switches in earth's magnetic field. Scientists predicted that if the seafloor spreads, a pattern of magnetic strips would be found in rocks around the Mid-Atlantic Ridge. This was proven true.

Learning Coach Guide
Lesson 6: Plate Tectonics

Your student will understand development of the theory of continental drift to the idea that earth's crust is divided into tectonic plates. The forces that shape the earth include movement in the mantle that affects earth's lithospheric plates. Your student will learn about the dramatic, volcanic events that occur at plate boundaries as a result.

Lesson Objectives
- Summarize the theory of plate tectonics.
- Summarize major scientific evidence for continental drift.

PREPARE

Approximate lesson time is 60 minutes.

Materials
For the Student

📇 Earth's Lithospheric Plates

pencils, colored 12

Keywords and Pronunciation

convection (kuhn-VEK-shuhn) : the transfer of heat by the circulation or movement of the heated parts of a liquid or gas

convergent plate boundary : a boundary at which tectonic plates are moving toward one another or colliding

divergent plate boundary : a plate boundary where two plates move away from each other

seismograph (SIYZ-muh-graf) : an instrument used to record earthquake waves

Theory of Plate Tectonics : the scientific theory that earth's crust is made up of about 20 huge plates that are always moving very slowly. According to the Theory of Plate Tectonics, all seven continents were once part of a super continent called Pangaea.

transform plate boundaries : a plate boundary where two plates move in opposite directions alongside one another

---

TEACH
Activity 1: Earth's Plates *(Online)*
Instructions
Your student will learn how scientists concluded that earth is composed of tectonic plates. This information led to a new theory of plate tectonics that explained the movement of continents and geologic activity such as earthquakes and volcanoes.

Activity 2: Forming a Theory *(Offline)*

Instructions

Your student will explore the theory of plate tectonics and earth's major lithospheric plates.

Answers to activity:

1. In 1912, research technology was not advanced, so it was difficult and took time to collect data about the earth. Also, scientists who did not want to accept the theory did not look more closely at it. Most of the information that supported the theory was discovered by accident.

2. In general, the more observations that support a theory, the more likely it is to be true.

3. Evidence from seafloor geography, including deep trenches and ridges and the locations of earthquakes and volcanoes, indicates the presence of tectonic plates.

4. If tectonic plates did not move, there would be very little action on the earth's crust. The fact that the earth experiences earthquakes, active volcanoes, and spreading ridges means that there is activity on the surface related to the motion of plates.

5: There are mountains at the boundaries of each pair of plates.

6. No, there are no mountains at the border of the Indian and Somali plates.

7. There is more earthquake activity between the South American and Nazca plates than the South American and African plates. We can conclude that the plates are moving differently at each boundary, producing very different levels of earthquake activity.

8. Answers will vary but should reference observations and records of geologic activity occurring on earth.

ASSESS

Lesson Assessment: Plate Tectonics (*Offline*)

Students will complete an offline assessment based on the lesson objectives. Print the assessment and have students complete it on their own. Use the answer key to score the assessment, and then enter the results online. The attached answer key is the most current and may not coincide with previously printed guides.

Name _____   Date _____

Plate Tectonics Lesson Assessment Answer Key

Read and answer each question below.

10 pts.

1. After Wegener proposed the theory of continental drift, evidence was found to support it that led to the theory of plate tectonics. List four pieces of that evidence.

   a. Seafloor spreading at mid-ocean ridges
   b. Reversing paleomagnetism in rocks on the ocean floor
   c. A seafloor that was geologically active with earthquakes, volcanoes, and mountain chains
   d. The location of earthquakes along plate boundaries

10 pts.

2. In your own words, describe the theory of plate tectonics and the action that occurs at plate boundaries. You may draw a picture to explain your answer.

The theory of plate tectonics explains that earth's continents move as part of plates in the lithosphere. Scientists have identified about a dozen major tectonic plates as well as some smaller ones. Where these plates interact, there are numerous earthquakes and volcanoes.

Learning Coach Guide
Lesson 7: Energy of Convection

Lesson Objectives

- Recognize that heat from the earth's interior reaches the surface through convection.
- Summarize the role of convection and gravity in the movement of plates.

PREPARE

Approximate lesson time is 60 minutes.

Materials

For the Student

    💻 Sources of Plate Motion

    pencil, colored - 1 red, 1 green.

    💻 Lesson Review

For the Adult

    💻 Lesson Review Answer Key

Keywords and Pronunciation

asthenosphere (as-THE-nuh-sfir) : the upper part of the earth´s mantle

convection (kuhn-VEK-shuhn) : the transfer of heat by the circulation or movement of the heated parts of a liquid or gas

convergent plates : plates that are moving toward one another

divergent plate boundary : a plate boundary where two plates move away from each other

gravity : a universal force that every mass exerts on every other mass

mantle : the part of earth that is beneath the crust and is made up of rock; about 84 percent of the earth´s volume is in the mantle

ridge push : at a divergent boundary, the pushing force on a tectonic plate caused by gravity acting on its elevated edge

slab pull : at a convergent boundary, the pulling force on a tectonic plate that causes its edge to sink into the mantle

subduction (suhb-DUHK-shuhn)

TEACH
Activity 1: Energy of Convection (Online)

Activity 2: Sources of Plate Motion *(Offline)*
Instructions
Using a world map of major lithospheric plates, your student will review the properties of oceanic and continental crust and identify transform and divergent boundaries between plates.

Answers to Sources of Plate Motion
1. Convection in the mantle and gravity acting on the edges of plates drive the motion of the plates.
2. In convection cells, matter that is cool is denser than surrounding matter and sinks. This pushes on the warmer, less-dense matter, which rises. This occurs over and over, creating a convection cell in which movement of fluid takes place.
3. The material in the mantle is more like a plastic, so it can flow.
4. At a mid-ocean ridge, plates move apart. Magma from the mantle below emerges as lava, which cools to form new ocean floor, filling the gap. The magnetic properties of the newly forming rock align with the magnetic field of the earth.
5. The Nazca plate is an oceanic plate. The South American plate is a continental plate. They are moving toward one another.
6. Answers may vary, but might include: a trench, where one plate pushes down under the other; mountains where one plate is pushed into folds or lifted up.
7. The Nazca plate is moving away from the Pacific plate.
8. A ridge, with a valley down the center and volcanic activity.
9. In both the geosphere and hydrosphere, hot, less-dense material rises. It cools, becomes denser, and sinks. In the geosphere, the material is slowly flowing solid rock in the mantle. In the hydrosphere, the material is liquid water.

Activity 3: Energy of Convection *(Offline)*
Instructions
In this activity, your student will review the concepts learned in this lesson. Store the review sheet in your student's Science Notebook.

ASSESS

Lesson Assessment: Energy of Convection, Part 1 *(Online)*
Students will complete an online assessment based on the lesson objectives. The assessment will be scored by the computer. The attached answer key is the most current and may not coincide with previously printed guides.

Lesson Assessment: Energy of Convection, Part 2 *(Offline)*
Students will complete an offline assessment based on the lesson objectives. Print the assessment and have students complete it on their own. Use the answer key to score the assessment, and then enter the results online. The attached answer key is the most current and may not coincide with previously printed guides.

Name   Date

Energy of Convection Lesson Review Answer Key

Fill in each blank with a term or name from the Word Bank. Use each term only once, but use all of the terms.

Word Bank

asthenosphere   convection

ridge   ridge push

slab pull   trench

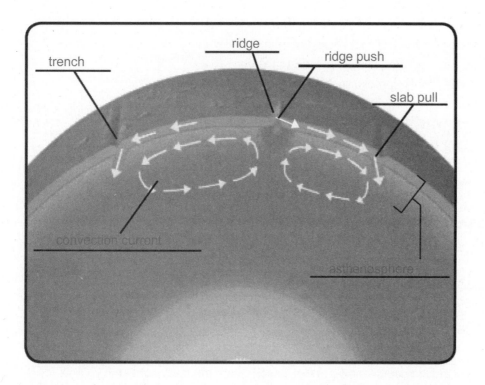

Name _____   Date _____

Energy of Convection, Part 2 Lesson Assessment Answer Key

10 pts.

1. Explain how gravity effects the movement of plates at mid-ocean ridges.

   Convection currents push up parts of the plate. Then, gravity pulls on those areas, bringing them downward. And, as these areas move lower, the ridges then push the plates away and outward.

10 pts.

2. How does convection in the asthenosphere contribute to the movement of tectonic plates?

   Convection causes currents in the asthenosphere. Heated rock, which is less dense, moves upward. Eventually, this hot rock will sink again, creating a circulating pattern. As the hot rock flows and circulates, the plates above it move as well.

Learning Coach Guide
Lesson 8: Plate Boundaries

Lesson Objectives

- Compare the properties of continental and oceanic crust.
- Describe the types of motion that occur at the boundaries of earth's plates.
- Interpret a map of plate boundaries on the earth.

PREPARE

Approximate lesson time is 60 minutes.

Materials

For the Student

- 📇 Lithospheric Plates
- 📇 Lesson Review

For the Adult

- 📇 Lesson Review Answer Key

Keywords and Pronunciation

Aleutian (uh-LOO-shuhn)

asthenosphere (as-THE-nuh-sfir) : the upper part of the earth´s mantle

convection (kuhn-VEK-shuhn) : the transfer of heat by the circulation or movement of the heated parts of a liquid or gas

convergent plates : plates that are moving toward one another

divergent plate boundary : a plate boundary where two plates move away from each other

Himalaya (hih-muh-LAY-uh)

hot spot : a hot place in the mantle where magma rises, often melting the crust above to form a volcano

lithosphere (LIH-the-sfir) : the rocky outer layer of the solid earth, averaging about 100 km in depth; the lithosphere includes the continents, islands, and the entire ocean floor

magnesium (mag-NEE-zee-uhm)

Mariana Islands (mar-ee-A-nuh)

San Andreas (san an-DRAY-uhs)

subduction (suhb-DUHK-shuhn)

transform plate boundaries : a plate boundary where two plates move in opposite directions alongside one another

TEACH
Activity 1: Plate Boundaries (Online)

Activity 2: Slow Motion: Divergent and Transform Boundaries (Offline)
Instructions
Using a world map of major lithospheric plates, your student will review the properties of oceanic and continental crust and identify transform and divergent boundaries between plates.

Answers to Slow Motion: Divergent and Transform Boundaries

1. Plates with mostly oceanic crust: Juan de Fuca, Philippine, Cocos, Nazca, Pacific, Antarctic, and Caribbean. Oceanic crust is thinner and denser.
Plates with a large amount of continental crust: South American, African, Arabian, Anatolian, Eurasian, Indian-Australian, and North American. Continental crust is thicker and less dense and the plate rides high on the asthenosphere.
2. The following borders should be red: between the African and South American plates; between the Pacific plate and the Nazca and Cocos plates; between parts of the Pacific and Antarctic plates. These are divergent boundaries.
3. The following borders should be green: between the Antarctic and South American plates; between the Pacific and the North American plate near California. These are transform boundaries.
4. Divergent motion, or motion of plates that are moving away from each other, results in undersea volcanoes and mid-ocean ridges.

Activity 3: Plate Boundaries (Offline)
Instructions
In this activity, your student will review the concepts learned in this lesson. Store the review sheet in your student's Science Notebook.

ASSESS

Lesson Assessment: Plate Boundaries, Part 1 (Online)
Students will complete an online assessment based on the lesson objectives. The assessment will be scored by the computer. The attached answer key is the most current and may not coincide with previously printed guides.

Lesson Assessment: Plate Boundaries, Part 2 (Offline)
Students will complete an offline assessment based on the lesson objectives. Print the assessment and have students complete it on their own. Use the answer key to score the assessment, and then enter the results online. The attached answer key is the most current and may not coincide with previously printed guides.

Name _____   Date _____

Plate Boundaries Lesson Review Answer Key

Review what you have learned about earth's spheres. When finished, place your completed lesson review sheet in your Science Notebook.

Review what you have learned about plate boundaries. Use the map above to fill in the table below. The first one has been completed for you.

Boundary	Type of Boundary	Types of Lithosphere at the Boundary	Description
1. North American – African	divergent	both are oceanic	The North American and African plates are moving apart.
2. Pacific-Philippine	convergent	both are oceanic	The Pacific and Philippine plates are colliding.
3. Indian-Eurasian	convergent	both are continental	The Indian and Eurasian plates are colliding.
4. Australian-Antarctic	divergent	both are oceanic	The Australian and Antarctic plates are moving apart.
5. Somali-African	divergent	both are continental	The African plate is splitting apart.
6. Pacific-North American	transform	Pacific is oceanic; North American is continental	The Pacific plate is moving along the North American plate at the San Andreas Fault.
7. Nazca-South American	convergent	Nazca is oceanic; South American is continental.	The Nazca plate and the South American plate are colliding, forming the Andes Mountains.

Name _____   Date _____

Plate Boundaries, Part 2 Lesson Assessment Answer Key

1. Explain why convergent oceanic plates subduct, but continental plates do not usually respond in this way.

   Oceanic plates are made of dense rock; therefore they sink into the asthenosphere more readily. Continental plates are made of lighter, more buoyant rock.

10 pts.

2. Complete the chart to compare different types of the plate boundaries. Add the words *transform, convergent,* and *divergent* to the chart.

Boundary Type	Description of Plate Motion
transform	plates slide past each other in opposite directions
divergent	plates move away from each other
convergent	plates move toward each other

Learning Coach Guide
Lesson 9: Landforms

Lesson Objectives
- Explain the relationship between geologic activity and plate motion.
- Identify the landforms that result from different types of motion at plate boundaries.

PREPARE

Approximate lesson time is 60 minutes.

Materials
For the Student
- Earth's Lithospheric Plates
- Lesson Review

For the Adult
- Lesson Review Answer Key

Keywords and Pronunciation
asthenosphere (as-THE-nuh-sfir) : the upper part of the earth's mantle
convergent plates : plates that are moving toward one another
divergent plate boundary : a plate boundary where two plates move away from each other
hot spot : a hot place in the mantle where magma rises, often melting the crust above to form a volcano
transform plate boundaries : a plate boundary where two plates move in opposite directions alongside one another

---

TEACH
Activity 1: Landforms *(Online)*

Activity 2: Slow Motion: Divergent and Transform Boundaries *(Offline)*
Instructions
Be sure to check your student's answers for this activity before he scores it for the assessment. Using a world map of major lithospheric plates, your student will review the events that occur at convergent boundaries. Your student will answer questions about plate boundaries.

Answers: Slow Motion: Convergent Boundaries
1. These are convergent boundaries. The following borders should be blue: between the Nazca and South American plates, between the Pacific and Philippine plates, between the Indian-Australian and Eurasian plates, between the North American and Pacific plates, between the Pacific and Eurasian plates, between the Pacific and Indian-Australian plates, and between the Philippine and Eurasian plates.

2. Any two of the following: the Nazca (oceanic) and South American (continental) plates, the Pacific (oceanic) and Philippine (oceanic) plates, the North American (continental) and Pacific (oceanic) plates, the Pacific (oceanic) and Eurasian (continental) plates, the Pacific (oceanic) and Indian-Australian (continental) plates, and the Philippine (oceanic) and Eurasian (continental) plates.
3. Mountains form where two continental plates collide.
4. A deep-ocean trench and volcanoes occur when one oceanic plate dives under another oceanic plate. Earthquakes are common there.
5. At convergent boundaries, plates collide with one another. At divergent boundaries, plates move away from one another. At transform boundaries, plates move alongside one another in opposite directions.

Activity 3: Landforms (Offline)

Instructions

In this activity, your student will review the concepts learned in this lesson. Store the review sheet in your student's Science Notebook.

ASSESS

Lesson Assessment: Landforms, Part 1 (Online)

Students will complete an online assessment based on the lesson objectives. The assessment will be scored by the computer. The attached answer key is the most current and may not coincide with previously printed guides.

Lesson Assessment: Landforms, Part 2 (Offline)

Students will complete an offline assessment based on the lesson objectives. Print the assessment and have students complete it on their own. Use the answer key to score the assessment, and then enter the results online. The attached answer key is the most current and may not coincide with previously printed guides.

Name _____ Date _____

Landforms Lesson Review Answer Key

Review what you have learned about earth's spheres. When finished, place your completed lesson review sheet in your Science Notebook.

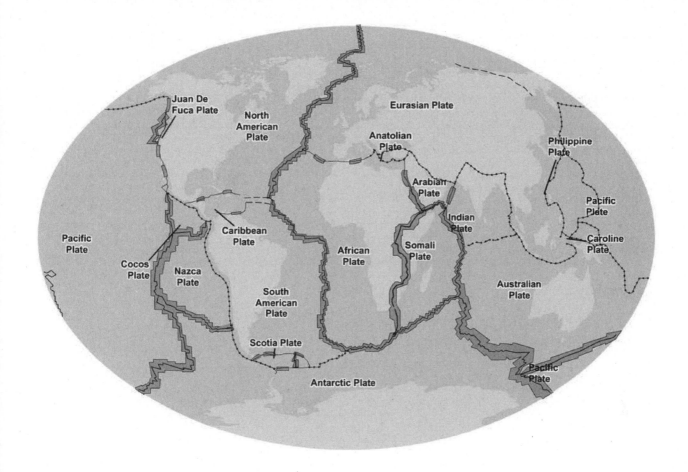

Review what you have learned about landforms. Use the map above to fill in the table below. You may also use the online World Map to help you. The first row has been completed for you.

Boundary	Type of Boundary	Volcanoes Likely?	Mountains Forming?	Trench Forming?
1. North American–African	divergent	no	no	no
2. Pacific-Philippine	convergent	yes	yes	yes
3. Indian-Eurasian	convergent	no	yes	no
4. Australian-Antarctic	divergent	yes	no	no
5. Somali-African	divergent	yes	no	yes
6. Pacific-Australian	convergent	yes	no	no
7. Cocos-North American	convergent	yes	yes	yes

Name _____   Date _____

Landforms, Part 2 Lesson Assessment Answer Key

10 pts.

1. Explain how convergent boundaries of oceanic crust form islands.

   As the oceanic plates come together, one plate may sink and slide beneath the other causing underwater volcanoes to form. As the magma cools slightly when it moves to the top of these volcanoes, the volcanoes will build up and gradually extend above the water's surface forming islands.

10 pts.

2. Identify the type of plate boundary and describe the plate motion that results in the formation of deep ocean trenches.

   The crust of two plates comes together at a convergent boundary in the ocean. One plate sinks below the other, and in the process, a trench develops.

Learning Coach Guide
Lesson 10: LAB: Plate Boundaries and Structural Geography

Using clay, your student will make a model of folded rock. When he cuts through the layers vertically and horizontally, he will see what folded rock looks like both from the side and from the top. The cuts represent what can happen when rock is eroded away in either direction, exposing the layered structure.

Lesson Objectives

- Identify the landforms that result from different types of motion at plate boundaries.
- Compare convergent, divergent, and transform plate boundaries.

PREPARE

Approximate lesson time is 60 minutes.

Advance Preparation

- If you don't already have it, you will need a 1 1/2 x 4 x 8 inch foam block for the Modeling Faults activity.

Materials

For the Student

    🖳 Modeling Folds Activity Instructions

    clay, modeling

    rolling pin

    ruler

    scissors

    🖳 Modeling Faults

    foam block

    knife (metal or plastic)

    markers or crayons

    pencils, colored 12

    🖳 Geologic Map

For the Adult

    🖳 Modeling Faults Answer Key

Keywords and Pronunciation

compression : stress on a material from a force or forces pushing inward from one or both ends

deformation (dee-fawr-MAY-shuhn)

shear : stress on a material from forces acting in opposite directions alongside one another

tension : stress on a material from a force or forces pulling outward from one or both ends

TEACH

Activity 1: Forces of the Earth *(Online)*

Instructions

Use this brief review to go over the forces of the earth. The terms in the review will help your student with the lab activities following.

Activity 2: Modeling Folds *(Offline)*

Instructions

Your student will make a model of rock folding and observe a cross section and top view.

Activity 3: Modeling Faults *(Offline)*

Instructions

Your student will use pushing, pulling, and sliding to examine different types of forces that create three types of faults: normal, reverse, and strike-slip. Your student will associate these forces and the resulting stresses in the crust with the fault formed.

Tips: Assist your student by cutting the foam block for him in this activity. Be sure that your student does not use the knife unsupervised or without permission.

Safety

Activity 4: Geologic Structure and Maps - Part 1 *(Offline)*

Instructions

Answers to Geologic Structure and Maps

1. Check to make sure student has colored each layer a different color for each corresponding letter.
2. Yes, it appears forces did affect these rocks. The rock layers are no longer flat. They have folds and faults.
3. The entire section appears to have been pushed, and subjected to compression, causing the rock to fold and causing a reverse fault on the right. The left side appears to have been pulled and later, subjected to tension, causing the normal fault.
4. The rock appears to have been pulled apart because the right side has a hanging wall. It has moved down compared with the left side, which has a footwall. This is a normal fault.
5. The rock appears to have been pushed together because the right side, which has a footwall, moved down compared with the left side. This is a reverse fault.

Activity 5: Geologic Structure and Maps - Part 2 *(Online)*

Instructions

Your student will apply what he has learned about plate motion, stresses in the earth, folding, and faulting to analyze the structural geology displayed in photos of actual places on earth. Print the Student Guide and Geologic Map to complete Part 1. Then use the photos online in Geologic Structure and Maps: Part 2 to complete the Activity. Make sure your student colors the layers of rock in all three sections. Your student will use the photos online to complete the activity Geologic Structure and Maps.

ASSESS

Lesson Assessment: LAB: Plate Boundaries and Structural Geography
(*Online*)

Review your student's responses on the Modeling Folds lab, the Modeling Faults lab and the Geologic Structure and Maps activities and input the results online. The attached answer key is the most current and may not coincide with previously printed guides.

Name _____   Date _____

Modeling Faults Answer Key

4. Block B is the foot wall.

5. Block A is the hanging wall.

6. Convergent

8. The blocks were pushed to make the reverse fault, but pulled to make the normal fault.

9. Block A is the hanging wall.

10. Block B is the foot wall.

11. Divergent

13. Transform

14. Normal fault

15. Reverse fault

16. Strike-slip fault

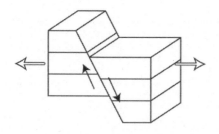

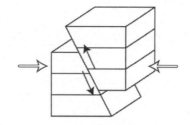

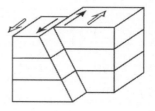

Name _____   Date _____

Lab: Plate Boundaries and Structural Geography Lesson Assessment Answer Key

Answers:

1. Answers will vary. Review your student's sketch in the attached Modeling Folds activity to determine if the lab activity procedures were followed in order to gather all pertinent data from the experiment.

2. Refer to your student's answer in the Modeling Faults activity: convergent.

3. Refer to your student's answer in the Modeling Faults activity: divergent.

4. Refer to your student's answer in the Modeling Faults activity: transform.

5.   normal fault   reverse fault   strike-slip fault

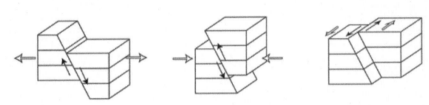

6. Refer to your student's answer the in Student Guide:
    Yes, it appears forces did affect these rocks. The rock layers are no longer flat. They have folds and faults.

7. Refer to your student's answer in the Student Guide:
    The entire section appears to have been pushed, and subjected to compression, causing the rock to fold and causing a reverse fault on the right. The left side appears to have been pulled and later, subjected to tension, causing the normal fault.

8. Refer to your student's answer in the Student Guide:
    The rock appears to have been pulled apart because the right side has a hanging wall. It has moved down compared with the left side, which has a footwall. This is a normal fault.

9. Refer to your students answer in the Student Guide.
    The rock appears to have been pushed together because the right side, which has a footwall, moved down compared with the left side. This is a reverse fault.

Learning Coach Guide
Lesson 11. Optional: Your Choice

Lesson Objectives

- Practice skills and reinforce concepts taught in this course.

PREPARE

Approximate lesson time is 60 minutes.

Learning Coach Guide
Lesson 12: Earthquakes

In this lesson, your student will learn about the causes of earthquakes and why they occur more often in some places than in others.

Lesson Objectives

- Explain causes of earthquakes.
- Explain the relationship between the speed of released energy waves in an earthquake and the material through which the waves move.
- Explain how scientists use seismic data to identify earthquake zones around the world.
- Explain how seismic data collected from earthquakes provide information about the earth's interior.

PREPARE

Approximate lesson time is 60 minutes.

Materials

For the Student

    📖 Locating the Epicenter

    ruler

    📖 Earthquake Review

For the Adult

    📖 Locating the Epicenter Answer Key

    📖 Earthquake Review Answer Key

Keywords and Pronunciation

epicenter : the location on the surface of the earth directly above the focus of an earthquake

fault : a fracture in which the pieces move relative to one another

focus : the zone within the earth where rock displacement produces an earthquake

fracture (FRAK-chuhr) : a break in the rock of the earth's crust

seismic waves : compression waves caused by movements in the earth's crust; seismic waves radiate outward from the source of an earthquake

seismogram : the record of an earthquake tremor, as recorded by a seismograph; by reading a seismogram, we can learn how powerful an earthquake is

seismograph (SIYZ-muh-graf) : an instrument used to record earthquake waves

TEACH
Activity 1: Earthquakes *(Online)*
Instructions
In this section, your student will read about how earthquakes are formed.

Activity 2: Locating the Epicenter of an Earthquake *(Online)*
Instructions
Using the arrival times of seismic waves at several seismograph stations, your student will locate the epicenter of an earthquake and make predictions like a real seismologist.

Activity 3: Earthquakes *(Online)*
Instructions
In this activity, your student will review the concepts learned in this lesson. Store the review sheet in your student's Science Notebook.

ASSESS

Lesson Assessment: Earthquakes, Part 1 (*Online*)
Students will complete an online assessment based on the lesson objectives. The assessment will be scored by the computer. The attached answer key is the most current and may not coincide with previously printed guides.

Lesson Assessment: Earthquakes, Part 2 (*Offline*)
Students will complete an offline assessment based on the lesson objectives. Print the assessment and have students complete it on their own. Use the answer key to score the assessment, and then enter the results online. The attached answer key is the most current and may not coincide with previously printed guides.

Name   Date

Locating the Epicenter of an Earthquake Answer Key

Materials

ruler

Introduction

All over the earth, seismographic stations keep their instruments operating all the time. By timing the arrival of P waves and S waves, scientists at each station can tell how far their station is from the source of any earthquake.

That distance is used as the radius of a circle around the station on a map of the world. The radius is the distance from the center of the circle to any point on the circle. By comparing the distance from several stations, seismologists can locate the earthquake's epicenter.

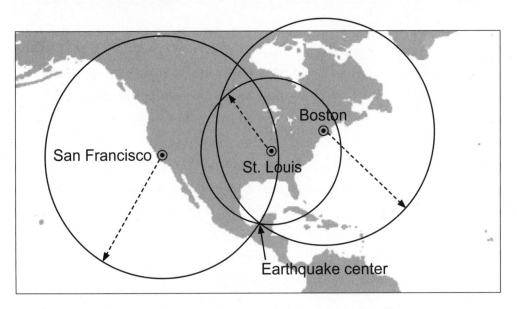

Look at the map. Notice that the three circles overlap. The location where they overlap is the approximate epicenter of the earthquake.

Procedure

1. Find the length of the radius of each circle. To calculate the radius, multiply the distance from the epicenter by 2, and then divide by 1,000 km.

Seismograph records were obtained from an earthquake in Central America. Using the information in the table, locate the epicenter on the map. You will need a compass and ruler. On this map, 1 cm is equal to 1,000 km.

Location of Station	Time Between Arrival of P and S Waves	Approximate Distance from Epicenter	Length of Radius of Circle (in cm)
Buenos Aires	1 min, 50 sec	1,600 km	3.2
Lima	3 min, 45 sec	2,400 km	4.8
Brasilia	4 min, 5 sec	2,880 km	5.8

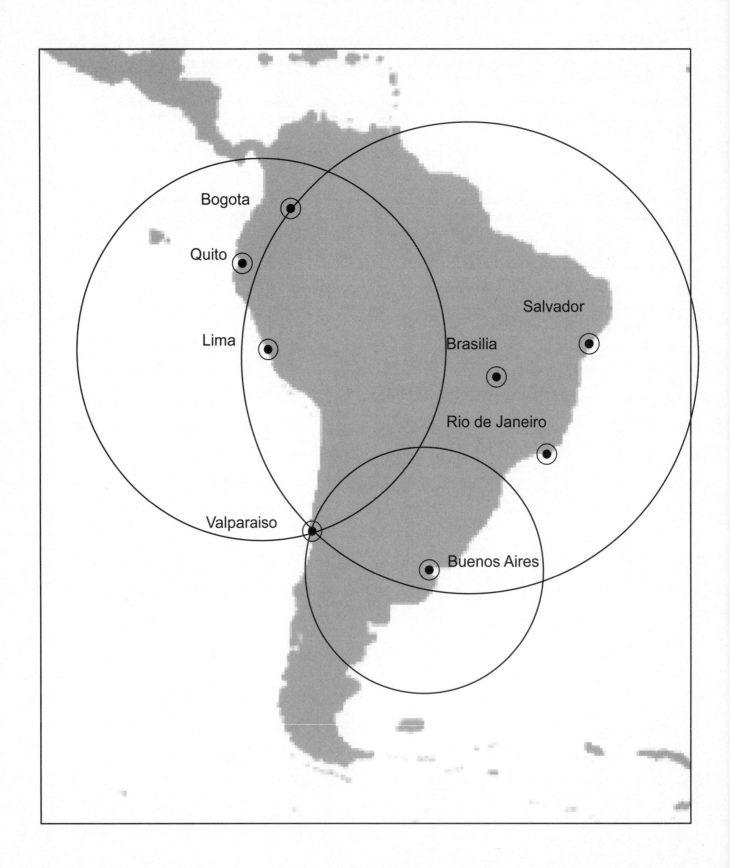

1. What city is near the epicenter?

   Valparaiso

2. List the properties of P waves and S waves.

   In P waves particles are squeezed together and pushed apart as they move. P waves move forward by compression; move through solids, liquids, and gases; and travel faster than S waves. S waves move up like a rope. S waves move up and down, move through solids only, and travel slower.

3. What conclusion would you draw if a seismogram from a particular seismic station showed only P waves?

   There is liquid between the earthquake and the seismic station.

4. Why is it better to use data from three or more seismic stations to find the epicenter of an earthquake?

   Comparing the data from several seismic stations helps locate the epicenter more accurately than with just one set of data. If just one circle is drawn from one set of data, that indicates the epicenter could be anywhere along that circle. More than one set of data helps pinpoint the epicenter.

Name   Date

Earthquakes Lesson Review Answer Key

Answer each question.

1. Fill in the illustration using the terms *epicenter*, *focus*, and *seismic wave*.

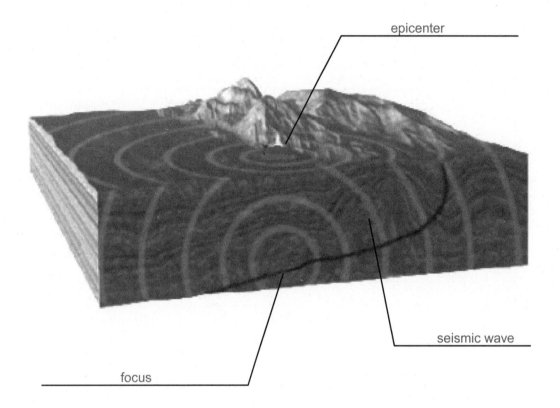

epicenter

seismic wave

focus

2. What causes an earthquake?

   Rocks along a fault build energy as the motion of tectonic plates places stress on them.

   An earthquake occurs when the stress is relieved by a sudden movement of other rock.

3. How is the epicenter of an earthquake related to its focus?

   The focus is the point where the earthquake occurs; the epicenter is the place on the

   surface directly above the focus.

4. How is energy from an earthquake carried to places far from its source?

   The energy of the moving rocks is carried as seismic waves through the rock around

   the focus.

5. Imagine that this earthquake occurred because the two parts of rock on either side of the fault
   were being pushed together. What kind of fault is this?

   Reverse fault

Earthquakes, Part 2 Lesson Assessment
Answer Key

1. How did scientists use seismic data to find out about the outer core of the earth?

   <u>They knew that S waves could not travel through liquid and also that S waves could not travel</u>

   <u>through the outer core of the earth. Scientists think, therefore, that the outer core must</u>

   <u>be liquid.</u>

2. When studying seismic records from all over the globe, what did scientists find out about the pattern of earthquakes?

   <u>Many earthquakes are concentrated in narrow zones along plate boundaries.</u>

   _____

   _____

Learning Coach Guide
Lesson 13: LAB: Using Seismographs

In this lab lesson, your student will construct a simple instrument and will experiment with earthquake engineering.

Lesson Objectives

- Construct a seismograph and explain how this device can detect earthquakes and other movements in the lithosphere.
- Analyze the importance of construction material and building shape in determining a building's performance and stability during an earthquake.

PREPARE

Approximate lesson time is 60 minutes.

Advance Preparation

- **Constructing a Seismograph**

- You may need several days to gather materials for this activity. Use the list below to figure out what you need.

- woodblock, approximately 20 cm x 10 cm x 4 cm

- yarn or string

- ink marker

- graph paper (10 pages)

- scissors

- table you can shake for testing (shake table)

- tape

- **Using a Seismograph in Earthquake Engineering**
- You may need several days to gather materials for this activity. A list of them are below so you can check off what you have and identify what you need.
- pipe cleaners
- brass fasteners
- craft sticks
- clay
- foam meat tray
- tape or tacks
- a table you can safely shake
- cardboard/paper pieces
- tape
- sugar cubes (1 box)
- mortar-like material: peanut butter, frosting, or double-sided tape
- cardboard
- window screen scraps (or other mesh material such as bags often used to hold produce).

Materials

For the Student

⌨ Construct a Seismograph

marker

block, wooden

graph paper

scissors

string

table

tape - masking

⌨ Earthquake Data Table

clay, modeling

cardboard

craft sticks

fastener, brass

foam tray

mortar-like material

pipe cleaners

seismograph

sugar cubes

window screen scraps

For the Adult

⌨ Earthquake Data Table Answer Key

TEACH
Activity 1: Earthquake *(Online)*
Instructions
Review concepts related to seismic activity.

Activity 2: Constructing a Seismograph *(Online)*
Instructions
In this activity, your student will explore the parts of a seismograph and how they work to measure seismic waves.

Activity 3: Earthquakes Cause Structural Damage *(Online)*
Instructions
In this brief activity, students will view pictures of structures that have been affected by earthquakes.

Activity 4: Using a Seismograph in Earthquake Engineering *(Offline)*
Instructions
Earthquake engineering is the science of building earthquake-proof buildings. Engineers design buildings to withstand the most movement and bumps. Students will examine building structures and materials to determine which are the most earthquake-proof.

ASSESS
Lesson Assessment: LAB: Using Seismographs (*Online*)
Review your student's responses on the Using Seismographs Lab and input the results online. The attached answer key is the most current and may not coincide with previously printed guides.

Name _____   Date _____

Earthquake Data Table Answer Key

Performance			
Wood		**Alone**	**After Stabilizing**
		Very weak, stood only under the smallest shakes. Foundation was easily moved.	Still very weak. While stronger with crossbraces, still easy to dismantle with gentle shakes.
Brick and Mortar	**1 story**	Strong, stood under heavy shakes. Foundation solid. When it fell, it crumbled.	Stronger. Prevented much of the collapsing upon movement in the foundation.
	2 story	Strong, but not as strong as 1 story. Collapsed with strong shake.	Stronger. Prevented much of the collapsing upon movement in the foundation.
	1-story L	Strong. Withstood strong shakes, not quite as big as square. Broke at inner corner of L.	Stronger. Prevented much of the movement but still ultimately collapsed at corner.
	2-story L	Strong, but not as strong as 1 story. Fell in again at inner corner of L.	Stronger. Prevented much of the movement but still ultimately collapsed at corner.
	Other shape	Not very strong. As soon as foundation was rocked, entire building crumbled.	Stronger. All corners were the weak spots, that made the building fall.
Steel		Very strong foundation that did not move. Upper floors swayed.	Still the strongest. Upper floors didn't move once reinforced.

Name _____   Date _____

Application:

Compare the seismograph readings for each test. Think about what you observed about each building. Decide which structural shape performs best during an earthquake. Decide which building materials perform best during an earthquake: ductile materials, such as steel and aluminum, or brittle materials, such as brick and stone?

Write your conclusions below. Include the following information:

- Which building shapes perform best during an earthquake? How did you learn this from your tests?

- Which building materials perform best during an earthquake? How did you learn this from your tests?

- Look at the photos of buildings that show earthquake damage. Choose three photos and make recommendations for how the buildings could have been made more "earthquake-proof."

Being able to build structures is important. I tested many different building materials, shapes, and constructions to see which structure could hold up to an earthquake. To measure the strength of the earthquakes, I built a seismograph to record seismic waves (table shakes). The pendulum of the seismograph swayed with the shakes of the table over the seismograph paper on the floor. The marker on the pendulum recorded the strength of the shakes.

The brick and steel structures performed better in the earthquakes than the wooden building. The one-story buildings did better than the two-story buildings. The rectangular shape was more stable than the L or other shape. Reinforcing helped the buildings hold up to stronger shakes. These results were shown by the seismograph, which recorded that larger and stronger shakes were required to destroy the better built houses.

These results show how to improve the structures in the pictures. Building #1 could be improved by cross bracing, like I did with the x-shape with craft sticks. Building #2 could be reinforced from the inside of the steel structure, like I did with ceilings and floors in the last test building. Building #3 would have been stronger with a different shaped stairwell, such as a rectangle, that could support the garage. The bricks in Building #4 needed to be reinforced from the inside of the wall.

Name _____   Date _____

Lab: Using Seismographs Lesson Assessment Answer Key

Answers:

1. Answers will vary. Review your student's responses in the Earthquake Data Table to determine if the lab procedures were followed in order to gather all pertinent data from the experiment.

2. Answers will vary.
   Sample answer:
   Being able to build structures is important. I tested many different building materials, shapes, and constructions to see which structure could hold up to an earthquake. To measure the strength of the earthquakes, I built a seismograph to record seismic waves (table shakes). The pendulum of the seismograph swayed with the shakes of the table over the seismograph paper on the floor. The marker on the pendulum recorded the strength of the shakes.
   The brick and steel structures performed better in the earthquakes than the wooden building. The one-story buildings did better than the two-story buildings. The rectangular shape was more stable than the L or other shape. Reinforcing helped the buildings hold up to stronger shakes. These results were shown by the seismograph, which recorded that larger and stronger shakes were required to destroy the better built houses.
   These results show how to improve the structures in the pictures. Building #1 could be improved by cross bracing, like I did with the x-shape with craft sticks. Building #2 could be reinforced from the inside of the steel structure, like I did with ceilings and floors in the last test building. Building #3 would have been stronger with a different shaped stairwell, such as a rectangle, that could support the garage. The bricks in Building #4 needed to be reinforced from the inside of the wall.

In the Application section of the attached Earthquake Data Table, did your student include how seismographs detect earthquakes and other movements in the lithosphere? *(10 points)*	
In the Application section of the attached Earthquake Data Table, did your student include the importance of construction material and building shape in determining how well a building will survive an earthquake? *(10 points)*	
Total *(20 points max)*	

Learning Coach Guide
Lesson 14: Unit Review

In this lesson, your student will review concepts learned in the unit before taking the Unit Assessment.

Lesson Objectives

- Describe the names, locations, and main characteristics of the layers that make up earth's interior.
- Recognize that movements in the earth's crust create seismic waves that scientists study to learn about earth's interior.
- Explain the historical development of the theory of continental drift.
- Describe evidence that supported the theory of continental drift.
- Describe key features of the theory of plate tectonics.
- Describe observations that the theory of plate tectonics explained what the theory of continental drift did not explain as well.
- Relate motion at the boundaries of earth's plates to the formation of landforms and geologic events.

PREPARE

Approximate lesson time is 60 minutes.

Keywords and Pronunciation

Theory of Continental Drift : the theory that the continents were previously joined together, and over time broke up and slowly drifted apart to their present positions

asthenosphere (as-THE-nuh-sfir) : the upper part of the earth's mantle

compression : stress on a material from a force or forces pushing inward from one or both ends

convection (kuhn-VEK-shuhn) : the transfer of heat by the circulation or movement of the heated parts of a liquid or gas

convergent plate boundary : a boundary at which tectonic plates are moving toward one another or colliding

convergent plates : plates that are moving toward one another

crust : the outermost, solid layer of any planet or moon

divergent plate boundary : a plate boundary where two plates move away from each other

epicenter : the location on the surface of the earth directly above the focus of an earthquake

hot spot : a hot place in the mantle where magma rises, often melting the crust above to form a volcano

magma : the molten or partly molten mixture of minerals, gases, and melted rock found below the earth's surface

ridge push : at a divergent boundary, the pushing force on a tectonic plate caused by gravity acting on its elevated edge

San Andreas (san an-DRAY-uhs)

seismic waves : compression waves caused by movements in the earth's crust; seismic waves radiate outward from the source of an earthquake

seismogram : the record of an earthquake tremor, as recorded by a seismograph; by reading a seismogram, we can learn how powerful an earthquake is

seismograph (SIYZ-muh-graf) : an instrument used to record earthquake waves

slab pull : at a convergent boundary, the pulling force on a tectonic plate that causes its edge to sink into the mantle

subduction (suhb-DUHK-shuhn)

tension : stress on a material from a force or forces pulling outward from one or both ends

Theory of Plate Tectonics : the scientific theory that earth's crust is made up of about 20 huge plates that are always moving very slowly. According to the Theory of Plate Tectonics, all seven continents were once part of a super continent called Pangaea.

transform plate boundaries : a plate boundary where two plates move in opposite directions alongside one another

---

TEACH
Activity 1: Plate Tectonics *(Online)*

Learning Coach Guide
Lesson 15: Unit Assessment

It's time for your student to take the Unit Assessment.

Lesson Objectives

- Describe the names, locations, and main characteristics of the layers that make up earth's interior.
- Recognize that movements in the earth's crust create seismic waves that scientists study to learn about earth's interior.
- Describe key features of the theory of plate tectonics.
- Relate motion at the boundaries of earth's plates to the formation of landforms and geologic events.
- Describe key features of the theory of plate tectonics.
- Explain the historical development of the theory of continental drift.
- Describe evidence that supported the theory of continental drift.

PREPARE

Approximate lesson time is 60 minutes.

ASSESS

Unit Assessment: Plate Tectonics, Part 1 (*Online*)

Students will complete an online assessment of the objectives covered so far in this unit. The assessment will be scored by the computer. The attached answer key is the most current and may not coincide with previously printed guides.

Unit Assessment: Plate Tectonics, Part 2 (*Offline*)

Students will complete this part of the Unit Assessment offline. Print the assessment and have students complete it on their own. Use the answer key to score the assessment, and then enter the results online. The attached answer key is the most current and may not coincide with previously printed guides.

Learning Coach Guide
Lesson 1. Optional: Your Choice

Earth contains many systems that interact to create the world we know. In this unit, your student will explore the atmosphere. The atmosphere is a thin layer of gases that surround and protect the planet. Your student will investigate weather and meteorology and explore global climates.

Lesson Objectives

- Practice skills and reinforce concepts taught in this course.

PREPARE

Approximate lesson time is 60 minutes.

Lesson Notes

Earth contains many systems that interact to create the world we know. In this unit, your student will explore the atmosphere. The atmosphere is a thin layer of gases that surround and protect the planet. Your student will investigate weather and meteorology and explore global climates.

Learning Coach Guide
Lesson 2: Layers of the Atmosphere

Your student will now turn to the atmosphere, that blanket of air that surrounds the earth. What are its layers? What gases make it up? What is air pressure, and how does it affect weather? What is ozone? The gases that surround us give us protection and allow us to breathe. Understanding atmosphere gives us the tools to understanding weather itself.

Lesson Objectives
- Identify the layers of the atmosphere.
- Describe the major components that make up earth's atmosphere.
- Describe the interaction of altitude, air density, air pressure, and temperature in the atmosphere.

PREPARE

Approximate lesson time is 60 minutes.

Advance Preparation
- If you don't already have it, please gather 2 large round balloons and a measuring tape.

Materials
For the Student
    📖 Investigating Temperature and Density
- advanced thermometer
- ice
- large bowl or pot
- large round balloon (2)
- measuring tape
- water

For the Adult
    📖 Investigating Temperature and Density Answer Key

Keywords and Pronunciation

air : a mixture of nitrogen, oxygen, and small amounts of other gases that surrounds the earth and forms its atmosphere

air pressure : the result of the weight of air in the atmosphere pressing down on earth

altitude : the height of an object above the surface of the earth

atmosphere : a blanket of gases that surrounds earth and certain other planets

aurora : streamers or bands of light sometimes visible in the night sky in northern or southern regions of the earth; scientists think an aurora is caused by charged particles from the sun that enter the earth´s magnetic field and stimulate molecules in the atmosphere

chlorofluorocarbon (KLOR-oh-flor-oh-KAHR-buhn) : any of several compounds of carbon, fluorine, chlorine, and hydrogen: used as refrigerants, foam-blowing agents, solvents, and in aerosol cans until scientists became concerned about depletion of the atmospheric ozone layer

density : the concentration of matter in an object or part of an object

exosphere (EK-soh-sfeer) : the top layer of the thermosphere

fluctuate (FLUHK-choo-eyt) : to shift back and forth

ionosphere (ahy-ON-uh-sfeer) : the region of the earth's atmosphere between the stratosphere and the exosphere

mesosphere (MEZ-uh-sfeer) : a layer of the atmosphere between the stratosphere and thermosphere, which lies between 50 and 80 kilometers (30 to 50 miles) above the surface of the earth

ozone (OH-zohn) : a form of oxygen which, in a layer in the stratosphere, screens out harmful ultraviolet rays from the sun

stratosphere : a layer of the atmosphere above the troposphere where temperature rises slightly with altitude

thermosphere : the topmost layer of the earth´s atmosphere that begins about 80 kilometers (50 miles) above the earth´s surface and extends into space

troposphere (TROH-puh-sfihr) : the atmospheric layer closest to the surface of the earth, which extends from the ground to between about 9 and 18 kilometers (6 and 11 miles) above the surface

---

TEACH
Activity 1: Layers of the Atmosphere *(Online)*
Instructions
Have your student read through the Explore on his own. Reinforce and explain difficult concepts as needed.
Explore Suggestions:
Check your student's understanding by asking the questions below:
1. Why is the atmosphere necessary for our survival? (*The atmosphere contains oxygen, which we breathe. It also protects us from the sun's deadly rays and from being hit by dust and rocks falling from space.*)
2. Why does air pressure decrease as you increase in altitude through the atmosphere? (*There is less air above pushing or exerting pressure down.*)

After this activity, check to see if your student can compare the layers of the atmosphere according to properties such as temperature and composition.

If your student has difficulty with any of these concepts, you may wish to review the Explore with him and have him explain the key points on each screen.

Activity 2: Investigating Air Pressure and Temperature *(Offline)*
Instructions
Your student will use a model to understand differences in density between cold air and warm air.
Tips
Review density with your student. Explain that an object with more matter packed into a certain amount of space is denser. Compare two common objects such as a whiffleball and a baseball or softball. Point out that they are about the same in size, but the baseball or softball has more matter packed inside.

ASSESS

Lesson Assessment: Layers of the Atmosphere, Part 1 (*Online*)

Students will complete an online assessment based on the lesson objectives. The assessment will be scored by the computer. The attached answer key is the most current and may not coincide with previously printed guides.

Lesson Assessment: Layers of the Atmosphere, Part 2 (*Offline*)

Students will complete an offline assessment based on the lesson objectives. Print the assessment and have students complete it on their own. Use the answer key to score the assessment, and then enter the results online. The attached answer key is the most current and may not coincide with previously printed guides.

Name _____   Date _____

Investigating Temperature and Density Answer Key

Atmospheric layers can be described by their altitude, density, temperature, and air pressure. In this activity, see how changes in temperature affect air density.

Materials

round balloon, 2

measuring tape

thermometer

ice

pot or bowl, large

water

Hypothesis

In this investigation, you will see how temperature affects air density in two balloons. Predict what will happen when one balloon is cooled in ice and the other is not. Why?

Answers will vary but should include reasons for the hypothesis. _____

_____

_____

Procedure

1. Blow up two balloons to the same size and tie them shut. Make sure they will be able to fit in the pot.

2. Use the measuring tape to measure the circumference (distance around the center) of both balloons. Record your measurements in cm in the data table.

3. Read the temperature of the thermometer. Record the temperature in °C next to "Starting temperature" for both balloons in the data table.

4. Fill the pot with ice and cold water to create an ice bath. Place one balloon and the thermometer into an ice bath for 10 minutes. Let the other balloon stay at room temperature.

5. After 10 minutes read the temperature of the thermometer in the ice bath. Record the temperature in the data table. Record the room temperature from your measurement in step 3.

6. Take the balloon and thermometer out of the ice bath.

7. Immediately measure the circumference of each balloon. Record the circumference in the data table.

8. Let both balloons stay at room temperature for five minutes. Observe both balloons.

9. Measure the circumference of each balloon again after five minutes. Record your measurements in the data table.

	Balloon 1: No ice bath	Balloon 2: Ice bath
Starting circumference		
Starting temperature		
Temperature after 10 minutes in ice		
Circumference after 10 minutes in ice		
Temperature after 5 minutes at room temperature		
Circumference after 5 minutes at room temperature		

Analysis

1. Describe what happened to the temperature and circumference of the balloon in the ice bath.

   The temperature and circumference both decreased in the ice bath.

2. Did any air escape from the balloon in the ice bath?

   No

3. Did the density of the air in the balloon increase or decrease because of cooling? Explain.

   The density of the air in the balloon increased because the molecules moved closer together. There were more molecules within a certain amount of space.

Conclusion

In this activity, you used a model to understand how temperature and density interact. The air in this experiment had equal amounts of air pressure.

In what way does the experiment model atmospheric layers?

   Among layers, the air in the atmosphere differs in temperature and density. This experiment involved changing air temperature and watching the effects on its density.

In what ways does the experiment **not** model atmospheric layers?

   The air in the experiment had equal amounts of pressure. In the atmosphere, pressure changes and is less in higher layers than in the lower layers.

Name _____ Date _____

Layers of the Atmosphere, Part 2 Lesson Assessment Answer Key

Directions: Answer the questions below.

(10 points)

1. In the space below, draw a diagram of the atmosphere labeling the stratosphere, troposphere, mesosphere, and thermosphere.

    Student drawing should show from the bottom the troposphere, stratosphere, mesosphere, and thermosphere.

(10 points)

2. Describe the change in air pressure and density as altitude increases in the atmosphere.

    As altitude increases, both air pressure and density decrease.

(10 points)

3. Describe how temperature fluctuates through the layers of the atmosphere.

    Temperature decreases in the troposphere, and then increases in the stratosphere due to ozone. Temperature decreases again in the mesosphere, and then rises again in the thermosphere.

Learning Coach Guide
Lesson 3: Conduction, Convection, and Radiation

Your student will learn about three ways heat is transferred on earth: conduction, convection, and radiation. These methods of heat transfer are related to weather.

Tips

Discuss with your student some examples of each type of heat transfer. Ask him to say which method of heat transfer is involved in the situations below.

- Snow melting in your hand (*conduction*)
- Earth heated by the sun (*radiation*)
- Water boiling in a copper tea kettle (*convection*)

Lesson Objectives

- Recognize that earth's heat energy (thermal energy) is distributed by convection, conduction, and radiation.
- Explain how heat energy is transferred from warmer to cooler places (in the air, water, and on land).

PREPARE

Approximate lesson time is 60 minutes.

Materials

For the Student

    🖳 Graph Paper

    lamp - gooseneck

    sand - 240 mL

    stopwatch

    advanced thermometer

    cups, paper - 12 oz (2)

    cylinder, graduated

    safety goggles

    water - 240 mL

For the Adult

    🖳 Heat Race Answer Key

Keywords and Pronunciation

conduction : the transfer of heat between two adjoining objects, caused by a temperature difference between the objects

convection (kuhn-VEK-shuhn) : the transfer of heat by the circulation or movement of the heated parts of a liquid or gas

electromagnetic radiation (ih-LEK-troh-mag-NEH-tik) : radiation consisting of electromagnetic waves, including radio waves, infrared, visible light, ultraviolet, X rays, and gamma rays

infrared (in-frah-RED) : radiation that lies outside the visible spectrum of light at its red end and has a wavelength between about 700 nanometers and 1 millimeter

radiation : the process in which energy is emitted by one body, transmitted through an intervening medium or space, and absorbed by another body

TEACH
Activity 1: Conduction, Convection, and Radiation *(Online)*
Instructions
Your student will review the transfer of heat energy by conduction, convection, and radiation among the air, land, and ocean.

Activity 2: Heat Race *(Offline)*
Instructions
Your student will conduct an experiment to study how air above land heats differently from air over the ocean. During the activity, he will create a model of radiation by placing a lamp over water and "land." He should refer to the lesson if he has trouble answering the questions that follow.

ASSESS

Lesson Assessment: Conduction, Convection, and Radiation, Part 1 *(Online)*
Students will complete an online assessment based on the lesson objectives. The assessment will be scored by the computer. The attached answer key is the most current and may not coincide with previously printed guides.

Lesson Assessment: Conduction, Convection, and Radiation, Part 2 *(Offline)*
Students will complete an offline assessment based on the lesson objectives. Print the assessment and have students complete it on their own. Use the answer key to score the assessment, and then enter the results online. The attached answer key is the most current and may not coincide with previously printed guides.

Name _____   Date _____

Heat Race Answer Key

Sample Data Table

Time in Minutes	Temperature of Sand in °C	Temperature of Water in °C
0	16.0	16.0
2	17.0	16.5
4	17.5	17.0
6	18.0	17.5
8	18.3	18.0
10	18.5	18.3

Conclusion

1. The sand or "land" should have warmed faster than the water.

2. Molecules of sand are closer together and can transfer heat to one another more quickly. Molecules of water are more spread out so heat does not transfer as well through the spaces between them.

3. Radiation

4. The heat source does not have to be in contact with matter to heat it. Radiated heat can travel through empty space without a liquid or solid to transfer it.

5. Due to convection, hot air over the land rises because it is less dense. Cooler air from over the water will move in to take its place until that air eventually heats up and rises.

Name   Date
_____   _____

Conduction, Convection, and Radiation, Part 2 Lesson Assessment Answer Key

Directions: Answer the questions below.

10 pts.

1. What does heat have to do with the circular movement of air in the atmosphere? Explain. You may draw a picture with your explanation.

   In the troposphere, air near the earth's surface is heated by conduction from the warm surface.

   Cool, dense air sinks toward the surface, forcing the warmer, less dense air to rise. The

   warmer air transfers heat upward as it rises. This type of heat transfer is called convection.

10 pts.

2. In the lesson activity Heat Race, how was conduction involved in the different temperatures of the sand and the water? Explain. You may draw a picture with your explanation.

   Molecules in sand are closer together and can conduct heat better than water molecules,

   which are spread out.

Learning Coach Guide
Lesson 4: Daily Weather

How do wind, humidity, air pressure, and temperature determine everyday weather? Your student will examine how these four characteristics interact to produce everyday weather. He will also measure the dew point of the air around him.

Lesson Objectives
- Define weather as the physical conditions of the atmosphere at a given location and time, as described by temperature, wind, air pressure, and humidity.

PREPARE

Approximate lesson time is 60 minutes.

Advance Preparation
- This activity takes place over a three-day period, but should not be started until the same day as the lesson.

Materials
For the Student
- Accurate Weather Reports
  - newspaper - local
  - newspaper - national
  - radio
  - telephone
  - television
  - websites

For the Adult
- Accurate Weather Reports Answer Key

Keywords and Pronunciation
condensation : the process by which water vapor changes from gas to liquid

dew point : the temperature at which the water vapor in the air would begin to condense to liquid, if the air were cooled to that temperature

humidity : the amount of water vapor in a given volume of air

precipitation : moisture, such as rain, snow, sleet, and hail, that falls from the atmosphere to the earth

relative humidity : the amount of water vapor in the air divided by the amount that would have to be present in the same air to form a cloud or condense on a surface

weather : the day-to-day conditions of an area, including the temperature, wind direction and speed, air pressure, relative humidity, and precipitation

TEACH
Activity 1: Daily Weather *(Online)*
Instructions
Your student will learn how temperature and air pressure lead to wind and humidity. These factors are used to describe the weather in an area.
Tips
- Have your student draw a concept map to show how temperature and air pressure are related.

Activity 2: Where Can I Get an Accurate Weather Report? *(Offline)*
Instructions
Your student will need access to a daily weather report from three sources such as television, radio, newspaper, Internet, or telephone. Your student may also compare three sources of the same type such as three different television or radio stations or three websites. The following links provide reliable weather information:

NOAA: National Weather Service

The Weather Channel

Activity 3: Daily Weather *(Offline)*
Instructions
In this activity, your student will review the concepts learned in this lesson. Store the review sheet in your student's Science Notebook.
Answers

1. low density : low pressure :: high density : **high pressure**
2. low pressure : rainy :: high pressure : **sunny**
3. high temperature : high humidity :: low temperature : **low humidity**
4. condensation : clouds :: precipitation : **rain (or snow, sleet, hail, etc.)**
5. solar energy : radiation :: wind : **convection**
6. cooling : contract :: heating : **expand**
7. hot air : rises :: cool air : **sinks**
8. air : air molecule :: water : **water molecule**
9. high humidity : low air pressure :: low humidity : **high air pressure**

ASSESS

Lesson Assessment: Daily Weather, Part 1 (*Online*)
Students will complete an online assessment based on the lesson objectives. The assessment will be scored by the computer. The attached answer key is the most current and may not coincide with previously printed guides.

Lesson Assessment: Daily Weather, Part 2 (*Offline*)
Students will complete an offline assessment based on the lesson objectives. Print the assessment and have students complete it on their own. Use the answer key to score the assessment, and then enter the results online. The attached answer key is the most current and may not coincide with previously printed guides.

Name _____   Date _____

Accurate Weather Reports Answer Key

A weather report is a description of weather for one day. A weather forecast is a prediction of weather in the future. What does a weather report contain? Each day, weather reports are available to you on the television, radio, newspaper, and the Internet. In this activity, you will compare weather forecasts from three sources and decide which is most accurate.

Hypothesis

Choose three sources from the list below. Of these three, which do you predict will give the most accurate weather description?

_____

_____

Materials

radio
television
local newspaper
national newspaper
phone
weather websites: www.weather.com, www.noaa.com

Procedure

1. Check each of your three sources for a report of today's weather. Record the information in Data Table 1.

2. Check each source for weather forecasts over the next three days. Record the information in Data Table 2.

3. Over the next three days, record the actual weather in Data Table 2.

4. If you need more room to record the weather, recopy the data tables into your Science Notebook.

Data Table 1

Today's Weather

Weather report source	Temperature	Wind speed	Relative humidity	Air pressure (high or low)	Precipitation

Data Table 2

Weather Forecasts over Three-Day Period

Weather report source	Day 1 Forecast	Day 1 Actual Weather	Day 2 Forecast	Day 2 Actual Weather	Day 3 Forecast	Day 3 Actual Weather

Analyzing the Data:

1. Look over the information in your table carefully. Compare the predicted weather with the actual weather.

2. Rank the weather sources from most accurate (1) to least accurate (3).

3. Explain why you ranked the weather report sources the way you did.

   Student should explain that the most accurate source had the best match between predicted weather and actual weather, while the least accurate had the worst match.

Conclusion

1. Which kind of weather report has the most information? Is this related to the type of report? Explain.

   Answers will vary; check student data.

2. What information do all of the reports include? Why is that information included in every weather report?

   Answers will vary; check student data.The information included in weather reports gives the best idea of how the weather will be on that day and how it could change.

3. Why does the accuracy of weather forecasts usually decrease as the number of days ahead increases?

   Weather can change over a few days.

4. What question did you explore in this activity? Can you answer that question now? How come?

   The question was which weather report was most accurate in reporting and predicting weather. The question can be answered now, at least for three sources because data was collected from three sources and compared over a three-day period.

Name   Date

Daily Weather, Part 2 Lesson Assessment Answer Key

Weather is a result of temperature differences all over earth. In the spaces below, explain how temperature is related to the following weather traits.

10 pts.

1. wind:

   The sun heats the earth unevenly so air is warmer at the equator than at the poles. Warm air rises, and cool air sinks. The movement of warm and cool air on earth leads to wind.

10 pts.

2. humidity:

   Humidity is the amount of water vapor in the air. Warmer air can hold more water vapor than cooler air. When air cools, water vapor condenses to form clouds or fog.

10 pts.

3. air pressure:

   Warmer air has less density and lower pressure. Cooler air is denser and has more pressure. The temperature of air affects its pressure and the weather that comes with it.

Learning Coach Guide
Lesson 5: Air Circulation

Lesson Objectives

- Describe the effect of earth's rotation on air circulation patterns.
- Define wind as the horizontal movement of air.
- Recognize that air moves from areas of higher pressure to areas of lower pressure.

PREPARE

Approximate lesson time is 60 minutes.

Materials

For the Student

    📖 Isobar Map

    📖 Working With Scientific Data: Isobars

    markers or crayons

For the Adult

    📖 Working With Scientific Data: Answer Key

Keywords and Pronunciation

air pressure gradient : the change in air pressure over a given distance

Coriolis effect (kor-ee-OH-luhs) : the curved movement of air or water caused by the rotation of the earth

friction : a force that resists motion between two objects that are in contact

isobar (IY-suh-bahr) : line on a weather map that connects areas of equal air pressure

TEACH
Activity 1: Air Circulation *(Online)*

Activity 2: Working With Scientific Data: Isobars *(Offline)*
Instructions

Your student will use data to remember how low- and high-pressure areas are related to weather patterns. He will associate these areas with the weather they typically bring.

High-pressure regions are usually associated with dry weather because as the air sinks it warms and the moisture evaporates. Low-pressure regions usually bring precipitation because when the air rises it cools and the water vapor condenses.

ASSESS

Lesson Assessment: Air Circulation, Part 1 (*Online*)

Students will complete an online assessment based on the lesson objectives. The assessment will be scored by the computer. The attached answer key is the most current and may not coincide with previously printed guides.

Lesson Assessment: Air Circulation, Part 2 (*Offline*)

Students will complete an offline assessment based on the lesson objectives. Print the assessment and have students complete it on their own. Use the answer key to score the assessment, and then enter the results online. The attached answer key is the most current and may not coincide with previously printed guides.

Name _____   Date _____

Working with Scientific Data: Isobars Answer Key

1. Refer to the map below.

2. Refer to the map below.

3. Areas of rain and snow would be the Midwest around Missouri and Nebraska, near Michigan, and in the northwest near Washington.

4. Clear skies would be found in the west near Nevada and California or in the northeast near Maine.

5. Refer to the map below.

6. Refer to the map below.

7. The direction would change from clockwise to counterclockwise.

8. The direction would change from counterclockwise to clockwise.

9. According to the map, high winds could be found around Illinois or near Colorado and Wyoming.

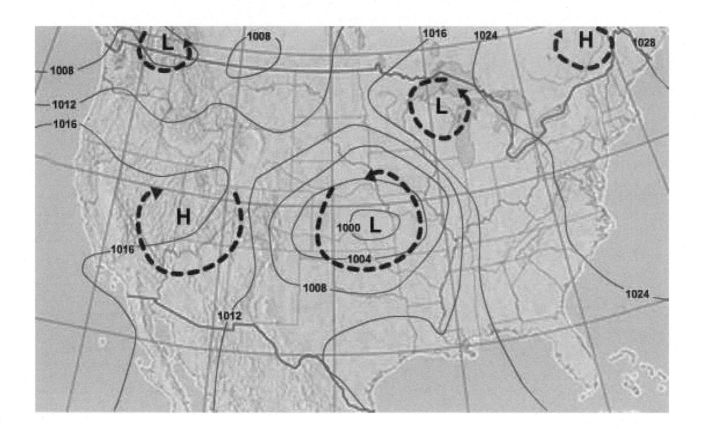

Name _____   Date _____

Air Circulation Lesson Assessment Answer Key

(10 points)

1.   In the space below, draw a simple globe. Label the poles and the equator. Then draw the routes of earth's global winds on its surface.

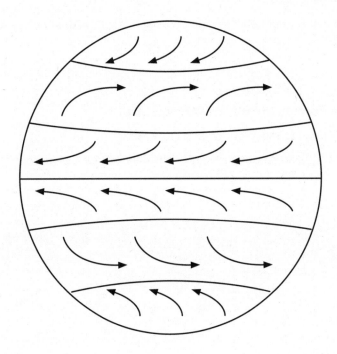

(10 points)

2.   Explain how earth's rotation affects the direction the wind travels from equator to pole and from pole to equator.

As earth rotates, air rotates with it. The equator is rotating faster than the poles. Air that starts rotating at the equator is moving faster when it reaches the poles, so it turns to the east. Air that starts rotating at the poles is moving slower when it reaches the equator so it gets behind and turns to the west.

Learning Coach Guide
Lesson 6: Air Masses

Your student may be familiar with weather maps and forecasts. He will learn how air masses interact to produce weather by focusing on the types of weather associated with four types of fronts and with high-pressure air and low-pressure air.

Lesson Objectives

- Locate and describe air masses on a weather map.
- Define an air mass as a large body of air characterized by nearly uniform temperature, humidity, and ground-level pressure.

PREPARE

Approximate lesson time is 60 minutes.

Materials

For the Student

  🖳 Air Mass Concept Map

   markers or crayons

   pencils, colored 12

   ruler

For the Adult

  🖳 Air Mass Concept Map Answer Key

Keywords and Pronunciation

air mass : a body of air covering a relatively wide area, with about the same properties through any horizontal section

front : a zone of transition between two different kinds of air masses

maritime : of or related to the sea

polar : of or relating to the North or South Pole

TEACH
Activity 1: Air Masses *(Online)*

Instructions

Earth's weather is affected by the movement of air masses, each having uniform temperature, pressure, and humidity throughout. Your student will identify these masses by name and describe their characteristics. After reading this section, your student should be able to:

- Name five kinds of air masses that affect North America.
- Describe four kinds of air masses in terms of temperature, humidity, and air pressure.
- Relate low- and high-pressure air masses to the general types of weather they produce.

Activity 2: Concept Maps *(Offline)*

Instructions

Your student will design a concept map to organize information about air masses. A concept map can show relationships between concepts in different ways. The best kind of map for this information is a spider map.

Tips:

- Suggest to your student that the map should show relationships between the type of air mass and where it originates (poles or tropics).
- If your student is having trouble getting started, use the answer key to draw parts of the map for him to fill in.

ASSESS

Lesson Assessment: Air Masses (*Online*)

Students will complete an online assessment based on the lesson objectives. The assessment will be scored by the computer. The attached answer key is the most current and may not coincide with previously printed guides.

Name _____   Date _____

Air Mass Concept Map Answer Key

Here's a riddle: what do you get when you cross a spider with a lot of new information? A concept map! (or a librarian with lots of legs).

Concept maps are a visual way of organizing information. They help you learn by showing facts "at a glance." Sometimes your brain can remember things more easily with a diagram or mental image. You've heard a picture is worth a thousand words, right? A concept map is worth at least ten-thousand.

Types of Concept Maps

What makes concept maps fun is their diversity and the different ways to show information. Take care to make sure you represent relationships correctly. Here are some examples of concept maps.

Map Description	What It Looks Like*
Spider map: The main idea is in the middle with supporting details arranged around it.	
Branching map: Big ideas appear at the top and supporting ideas are organized below.	
Flow chart: This shows the steps of a process in order.	

*You can choose whatever shapes and colors you want to use for your concept map.

Tips for Making a Concept Map

1. Gather paper, markers, and a ruler and some shapes to trace (optional).

2. Get your reference materials ready. In this activity, you will use information from your Science lessons.

3. Be familiar with the different types of concept maps so you know which one best represents this information.

4. Relax and visualize the information in your head.

5. Try sketching a diagram in pencil first.

6. You might need to draw more than one map, or think of ways to connect smaller maps to show all of the information.

7. Use colors or shapes to show differences between main ideas and supporting details.

8. Check to see that your map is clear and makes sense to you. If not, revise it!

Make the Map

Now you will make a concept map. Your concept map will organize information about four types of air masses. Use the word bank below to help you. You may want to include additional vocabulary and ideas.

Word Bank

continental	polar	tropical	maritime
humid	dry	air mass	pressure
weather	warm	temperature	cold
dense	pressure	latitude	high
low	precipitation		

1. What kind of map do you think is best to use to organize information about four kinds of air masses? Why did you choose that map?

    Your student should choose a spider map to display information about air masses.

3. In your Science Notebook or on a piece of blank paper, begin your concept map. When finished, show your map to an adult to check your work.

    Your student's map may not look exactly like the one below. Check to see that the information below is included and represented correctly.

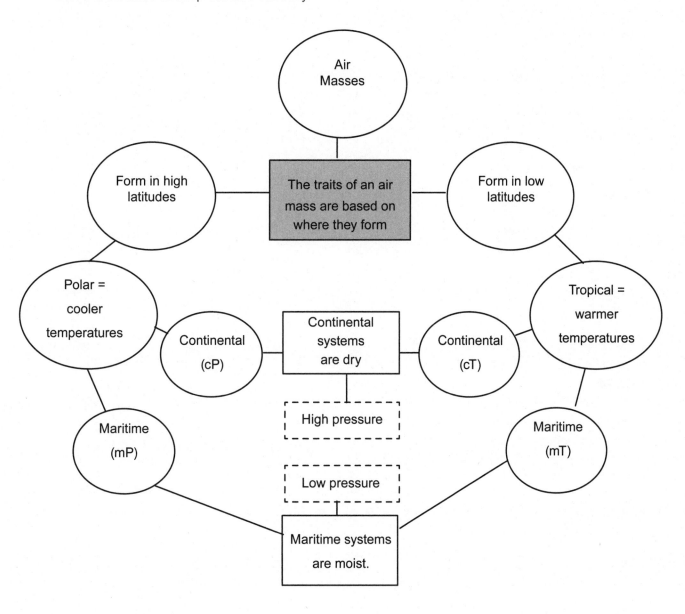

4. Remember: the best map is one that makes sense to you. Your map may not look exactly like one that another person has made, but that's okay. Concept maps are helpful when you want to show important concepts and how these ideas are related.

Learning Coach Guide
Lesson 7: Weather Fronts

Next in your student's continuing study of the atmosphere is the topic of fronts and meteorology. Understanding the types and interactions of air masses gives valuable information to predicting the weather. Your student will learn how air masses interact to produce weather by focusing on the types of weather associated with four types of fronts and with high-pressure air and low-pressure air.

Lesson Objectives

- Describe how air masses interact at cold, warm, stationary, and occluded fronts.
- Describe typical weather details associated with cold, warm, stationary, and occluded fronts.

PREPARE

Approximate lesson time is 60 minutes.

Materials

For the Student

    📖 Exploring Fronts

Optional

    computer

For the Adult

    📖 Exploring Fronts Answer Key

Keywords and Pronunciation

cold front : the zone separating two air masses, of which the cooler, denser mass is advancing and replacing the warmer

isobar (IY-suh-bahr) : line on a weather map that connects areas of equal air pressure

occluded front (uh-KLOOD-uhd) : a front that forms when warm air is wedged upward between two cold fronts

stationary front : a front between warm and cold air masses that is moving very slowly or not at all

warm front : a transition zone between a mass of warm air and the colder air it is replacing

TEACH
Activity 1: Weather Fronts (Online)

Instructions

Have your student read through the Explore on his own. Reinforce and explain difficult concepts as needed.

Explore Suggestions:

Check your student's understanding by asking the following questions:

1. Complete the sentence: At warm fronts, warm air, which is _____ dense than cold air, moves _____ and thunderclouds form. (*less, up*)
2. Complete the sentence: At cold fronts, cold air, which is _____ dense than warm air, forces the warm air up. (*more*)
3. At which front do the most dramatic weather events occur? (*cold*)

After this activity, check to see if your student can do the following:

- Identify the four types of fronts (cold, warm, stationary, and occluded) and describe how air masses interact.

If your student has difficulty with any of these concepts, you may wish to review the Explore with him and have him explain the key points on each screen.

Activity 2: Exploring Fronts (Offline)

ASSESS

Lesson Assessment: Weather Fronts (Offline)

Students will complete an offline assessment based on the lesson objectives. Print the assessment and have students complete it on their own. Use the answer key to score the assessment, and then enter the results online. The attached answer key is the most current and may not coincide with previously printed guides.

Name _____   Date _____

Exploring Fronts Answer Key

A table is one way to organize a lot of new information. Use the lesson and the table below to organize what you have learned about fronts. You may write into the table on this sheet or create a new table using a computer program.

Front	How Air Masses Interact	Weather
Warm	Warm air masses move in and replace cold air masses	Drizzly rain or snow
Cold	Cold air masses move against and replace warm air masses	Rain or snow
Stationary	When warm and cold fronts meet at a standstill	Rain, snow, wind all lasting a long time
Occluded	A cold front meets a warm front that is following another cold front and forces warm air up in a wedge	Rain and snow

Name _____   Date _____

Weather FrontsLesson Assessment Answer Key

Next to each statement, fill in the type of front that is described (cold, warm, stationary, or occluded).

(2 points)
1. _____warm front_____ Warm, less-dense air rises gradually above cooler air.

(2 points)
2. _____stationary front_____ Rainy or snowy weather lasts a very long time at this front.

(2 points)
3. _____cold front_____ Denser, colder air pushes in under warm air.

(2 points)
4. _____warm front_____ Weather may be drizzly or snowy.

(2 points)
5. _____stationary front_____ Cold and warm air are next to each other, but are at a standstill.

(2 points)
6. _____occluded front_____ Warm air is forced up in a wedge between two masses of cold air.

(2 points)
7. _____cold front_____ This kind of air mass usually brings thunderclouds and storms.

Use the map below to answer question 8.

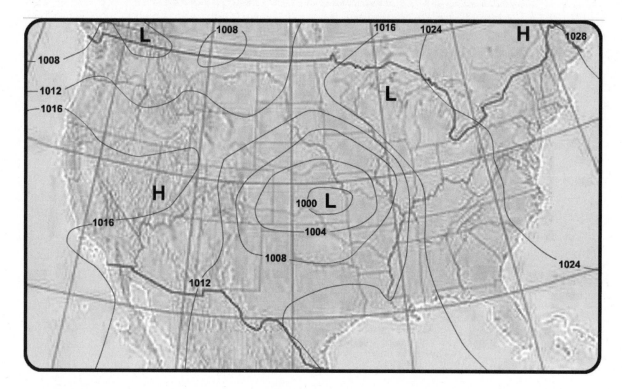

(10 points)

8. A high pressure system is sitting over the coast of Virginia in early summer. How would the weather change if a cold front moves into this area?

The weather on the coast of Virginia is probably warm and dry. A cold front would likely bring

rain or rainstorms. Since early summer is warm or hot in Virginia, snow is unlikely.

Learning Coach Guide
Lesson 8: Meteorology

In this lesson, your student will work with symbols used to explain weather on weather maps. Then he will use weather maps to describe weather in different locations.

Lesson Objectives

- Given weather data for a particular location, develop a weather forecast for that area.
- Interpret weather symbols and isobars on a weather map to describe the weather in a given location.

PREPARE

Approximate lesson time is 60 minutes.

Materials

For the Student
> 💻 U.S. Weather Map

For the Adult
> 💻 Investigating Weather Maps Answer Key

Keywords and Pronunciation

barometer (buh-RAH-muh-tuhr) : a tool used to measure air pressure

hygrometer (hiy-GRAH-muh-tuhr) : a tool used to measure the amount of humidity, or moisture, in the air

isobar (IY-suh-bahr) : line on a weather map that connects areas of equal air pressure

meteorologist (mee-tee-uh-RAH-luh-jist) : a scientist who studies weather and reports on weather conditions

---

TEACH
Activity 1: Meteorology (Online)

Activity 2: Investigating Weather Maps (Offline)
Instructions
Your student will study a weather map of the United States. He will answer questions about what types of weather cold and warm fronts bring. He may refer to the lesson text here or in previous lessons for help.
Tips
- Check your student's work to be sure he understands the interactions between low- and high-pressure air and the weather they bring.

ASSESS

Lesson Assessment: Meteorology (*Online*)
Students will complete an online assessment based on the lesson objectives. The assessment will be scored by the computer. The attached answer key is the most current and may not coincide with previously printed guides.

Name _____   Date _____

Investigating Weather Maps Answer Key

Interpreting Weather Maps

1. stormy

2. The temperature of the air will fall, and the air pressure will rise.

3. yes

4. nimbostratus

5. drizzly rain

6. Your student should draw a symbol for a stationary front.

7. warm, clear, and dry

8. The advancing warm front may pass northward, bringing warmer, milder weather. However, the cold front may advance eastward, with the low pressure system. As the cold front approaches, it may bring lower pressure and stormy weather.

9. Because there are so many things involved in weather—pressure, moisture, and temperature—a small change in one can cause a large, unexpected change in the weather.

Name _____   Date _____

Air Masses and Fronts

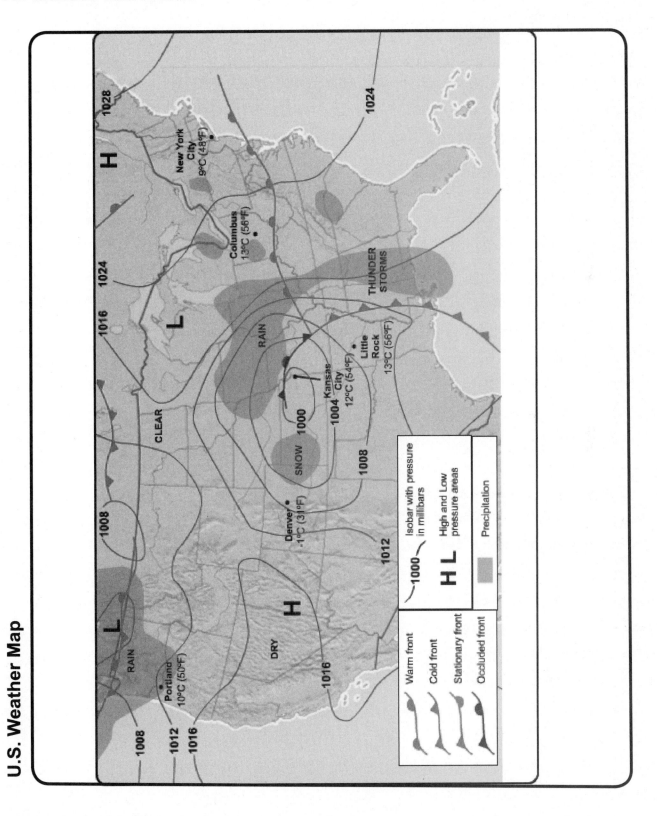

U.S. Weather Map

Learning Coach Guide
Lesson 9: LAB: Working with Weather

Lesson Objectives

- Conduct investigations using weather measurement devices.
- Collect and use data to analyze the weather.

PREPARE

Approximate lesson time is 60 minutes.

Materials

For the Student

- Build a Barometer
- Graph Paper
   - drinking straw
   - jar, glass - without lid
   - large round balloon
   - rubber bands, thick
   - ruler
   - safety goggles
   - scissors
   - tape - masking
   - toothpicks
- U.S. Weather Maps

For the Adult

- Build a Barometer Answer Key
- Weather Forecasting Answer Key

Keywords and Pronunciation

barometer (buh-RAH-muh-tuhr) : a tool used to measure air pressure

millibar : a centimeter-gram-second unit of pressure equal to one thousandth of a bar or 1,000 dynes per square centimeter, used to measure air pressure

TEACH
Activity 1: Build a Barometer *(Online)*

Activity 2: Build a Barometer *(Offline)*

Instructions

Your student will create a barometer to measure air pressure. He will measure and track the air pressure for 10 days, and draw conclusions based on the data. Since the activity takes a few days to complete, you may wish to complete the rest of the lesson and come back to this part when all data have been collected.

Science Club Idea

Communication and working together is paramount to scientific investigation and study. Help your student practice these skills by connecting with other Earth Science students during this activity and comparing your student's measurements to theirs. Or, work with your teacher to connect with students in other geographic locations to discuss their results either by message board or in a live session.

Activity 3: Working With Scientific Data: Weather Forecasting *(Offline)*

Instructions

Your student will interpret weather information to create a weather map and predict a four-day forecast. This can be a challenge as your student must handle many pieces of information. The focus should be on using correct symbols for fronts and air pressure and showing movement of weather from west to east.

Tips
- Encourage your student to have fun with the activity.
- Provide a supplemental map that lists state names.
- Refer to earlier lessons in the unit to review weather symbols.
- Focus on prediction skills using data rather than creating an exact forecast.
- Remind your student that meteorologists must make weather maps with similar data and together appreciate the challenge of this task.

ASSESS

Lesson Assessment: LAB: Working with Weather (*Online*)

Review your student's responses on the Build a Barometer and Working with Scientific Data: Weather Forecasting labs and input the results online. The attached answer key is the most current and may not coincide with previously printed guides.

Name _____   Date _____

Weather Forecasting Answer Key

Note: Answer Key does not show precipitation.
You may check http://www.hpc.ncep.noaa.gov/dailywxmap/index.html for precipitation for
July 4 to July 7, 2006.

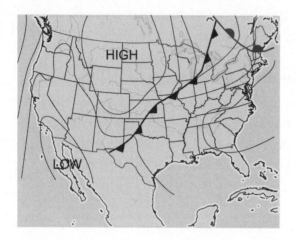

July 4, 2006 _____

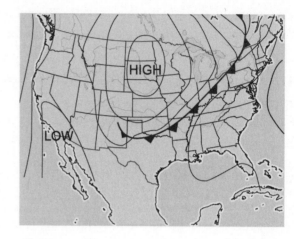

July 5, 2006 _____

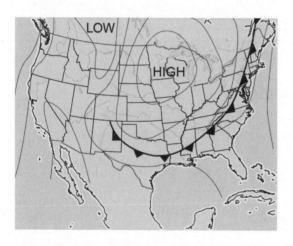

July 6, 2006 _____

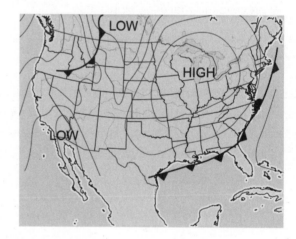

July 7, 2006 _____

Name _____   Date _____

Build a Barometer Answer Key

Introduction

Using some simple household materials, you can construct a working barometer. Your reading will not be exact without mercury, but you can get an idea of the rise and fall of air pressure and of the related changes in weather.

Materials

glass jar without lid
large balloon
thick rubber band
drinking straw
masking tape
ruler
toothpick
scissors

Procedure

Build the Barometer

1. Using the scissors, cut the neck off the balloon. Throw the neck of the balloon away.

2. Carefully stretch the large piece of the balloon over the opening of the jar.

3. Use the rubber band to hold the stretched balloon firmly in place over the opening of the jar.

4. Tape the toothpick to the straw so that it is pointing from one end of the straw.

5. Tape the other end of the straw to the center of the balloon. Your barometer is now complete!

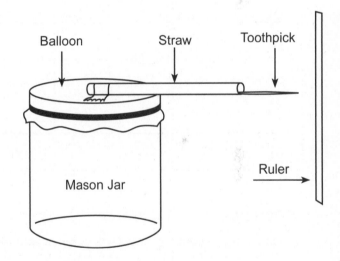

Taking Measurements

6. Find a flat place outside where you can set your barometer for the next 10 days.

7. Hold the ruler vertically on a flat surface, with the "0" at the bottom. Measure the height of the toothpick, in millimeters.

8. Record the data in the data table and write a brief description of today's weather (dry, rainy, windy, etc.).

9. Repeat steps 7 and 8 for the next nine consecutive days. Try to take readings at the same time each day.

Data Table

Day	Time	Height of Toothpick in mm	Current Weather Conditions

Analysis:

Using the graph paper, create a line graph of your data. Along the bottom, write a number for each day. Along the left side, add numbers from 1–25. Place a dot above each day at that day's measurement, and then connect the dots.

Tip: You may trim the graph paper and glue it onto another piece of paper if you need more room or less boxes.

Conclusion

1. Explain how your barometer worked. How was this different from a real barometer?

   As air pressure rises, it pushes down on the balloon causing the end of the straw with the toothpick to rise. As air pressure falls, the air inside the jar can spread out, making the balloon bulge and causing the end of the straw to drop lower. A real barometer uses mercury to measure the rise and fall of air pressure.

2. What relationship did you notice between the height of the toothpick and the current weather conditions at the time of testing?

   Answers will vary but in general low pressure results in unstable weather conditions while high pressure usually brings dry weather.

3. If the height of the toothpick was very low, what kind of weather would you expect to experience?

   When the toothpick height is low the pressure outside the jar is low and one could predict a storm or rain to follow.

Science Club Idea

Communication and working together are important scientific skills. Use your school's message board to find out about other Earth Science students' results from this activity. Or, talk to your teacher to find students in other cities or states and compare your air pressure measurements to theirs.

Name _____   Date _____

LAB: Working with Weather Lesson Assessment Answer Key

Answers:

1. Depending on the evidence collected, data entered into the table will vary. In order to receive full credit, please make sure your student collected data for 10 days using the homemade barometer. Award 1 point for each day data was collected.

2. Your student should have constructed a line graph representing the data he collected. Depending on the evidence collected, data entered into the line graph will vary. Award 1 points for constructing the graph with the number for each day on the bottom line, 1 point for labeling the left side 1-25, and then 8 points for properly representing the data collected.

3. As air pressure rises, it pushes down on the balloon causing the end of the straw with the toothpick to rise. As air pressure falls, the air inside the jar can spread out, making the balloon bulge and causing the end of the straw to drop lower. A real barometer uses mercury to measure the rise and fall of air pressure.

4. Answers will vary but in general low pressure results in unstable weather conditions while high pressure usually brings dry weather.

5. When the toothpick height is low, the pressure inside the jar is low and one could predict a storm or rain to follow.

6. Resonable weath maps shown below (answers may vary):

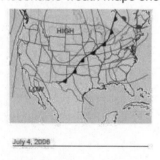

July 4, 2006 _____

July 5, 2006 _____

July 6, 2006 _____

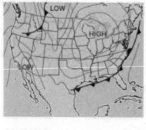

July 7, 2006 _____

7. Answers will vary but in general low pressure results in unstable weather condistions while high pressure usually brings dry weather. With a high pressure system moving in, predictions for dry weather are expected.

8. Answers will vary but should include the idea that it is difficult to be 100% accurate when predicting the weather because several factors (including winds, air movement, mountains, large bodies of water, and high elevations) influence weather on a daily basis.

Learning Coach Guide
Lesson 10. Optional: Your Choice

Lesson Objectives

- Practice skills and reinforce concepts taught in this course.

PREPARE

Approximate lesson time is 60 minutes.

Learning Coach Guide
Lesson 11: Weather and Climate

Climate is the long-term average of atmospheric conditions for a given region as described by weather observations. In this lesson, your student will investigate climate types that affect the earth and begin exploring influences on global climate.

Lesson Objectives

- Define climate as the long-term average of atmospheric conditions for a given region as described by weather observations.
- Contrast weather and climate.
- Describe and locate on a world map the main climate types (polar, temperate, and tropical).
- Explain the influence of latitude on climate conditions and patterns.

PREPARE

Approximate lesson time is 60 minutes.

Materials

For the Student
- Climate Data Chart
- K12 Wall Map
- markers or crayons
- self-sticking notepad
- Climate Around the World

For the Adult
- Climate Around the World Answer Key

Keywords and Pronunciation

climate : the long-term pattern of weather over time for a particular area, including temperature and precipitation

climate zone : area on earth that has similar temperature, rainfall, snowfall, and sunshine

climatologist (kliy-muh-TAH-luh-jist) : a scientist who studies long-term weather patterns

weather : the day-to-day conditions of an area, including the temperature, wind direction and speed, air pressure, relative humidity, and precipitation

TEACH
Activity 1: Weather and Climate (Online)

Instructions

Latitude, ocean currents, and altitude are factors that affect climate. Zones of particular climates around the world are mapped based on precipitation and temperature data. As your student reads, he will follow the directions to label each city or place on his U.S. Wall Map as he reads through this lesson.

Activity 2: Climates Around the World (*Offline*)
Instructions

A number of factors contribute to differences in climate in different places on earth. Your student will find the average yearly temperature and rainfall for several cities around the world. He will then answer questions comparing cities with similar latitudes but different climates. Be aware, and help your student appreciate, that this exercise just skims the surface of considerations about climate. Most notably, we are not emphasizing variations during the year, which provide an important dimension to climate.

Tips

- If the World Climates website is not working, your student can find data using the answer key.
- Certain entries at the World Climates website do not match the listed location. For example, Addis Ababa, Ethiopia, might display as Addis Ababa, Ethiopia, and Eritrea. All cities can be found at the site, so encourage your student to look carefully for the correct city.

ASSESS

Lesson Assessment: Weather and Climate (*Online*)

Students will complete an offline assessment based on the lesson objectives. Print the assessment and have students complete it on their own. Use the answer key to score the assessment, and then enter the results online. The attached answer key is the most current and may not coincide with previously printed guides.

Name _____   Date _____

Climate Around the World Answer Key

Use the map on page 3 and the Internet to record and study the climates of different regions around the globe.

1. Use latitude and longitude to label each city on your map.

2. Visit the World Climate website to find climate information about your city.

3. Record the average yearly climate and total yearly precipitation information in the chart.

4. Answer the questions.

City	Average Yearly Temperature in °C	Total Yearly Precipitation in mm
Minsk, Belarus (Former USSR) (53° N, 27° E)	5.5	678.3
Shanghai, China (31° N, 121° E)	15.4	1144.3
Addis Ababa, Ethiopia (8° N, 38° E)	16.5	1229.5
Helsinki, Finland (60° N, 24° E)	4.5	635.4
Banff, Canada (51° N, 115° W)	2.1	461.9
Kuala Lumpur, Malaysia (3° N 101° E)	26.5	2393.6
Buenos Aires, Argentina (34° S, 58° W)	16.6	1005.2
Jakarta, Indonesia (6° S, 106° E)	26.5	1821.0

Questions

1. What factor contributes most to the warm climate of Kuala Lumpur?

   Kuala Lumpur is located near the equator, where the sun's energy is intense all year.

2. Banff and Minsk are located at similar latitudes. What could account for Banff's average yearly temperature being lower than Minsk's?

   Banff is located in the Rocky Mountains in Canada, at a higher elevation above sea level than

   Minsk. Cities in or near mountains, at higher elevations, tend to be cooler.

3. Which city's climate is most similar to Jakarta; Addis Ababa or Kuala Lumpur? Explain your answer.

   Kuala Lumpur's climate is most like Jakarta. Their average yearly temperatures are the same

   and both are located on coasts where warm ocean breezes can bring moisture and higher

   rainfall. Addis Ababa is located at slightly higher latitude and is inland so it experiences lower

   temperatures and rainfall than Jakarta and Kuala Lumpur.

4. Shanghai and Buenos Aires are located thousands of miles apart and in different hemispheres. Yet their climates are similar. What reasoning could explain this?

   Shanghai and Buenos Aires are located the same distance away from the equator and so they

   have similar climates.

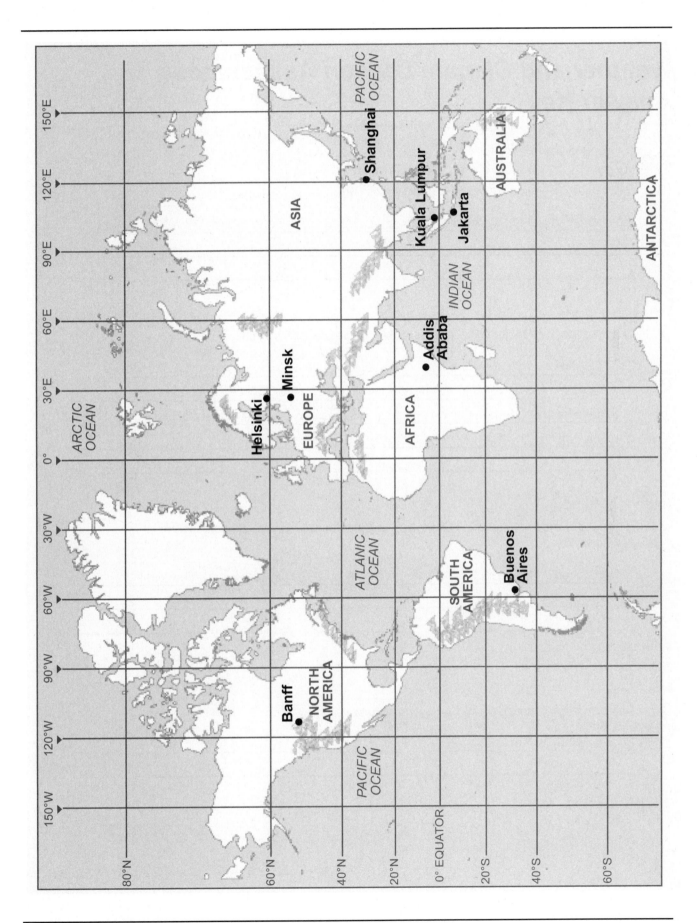

Name _____   Date _____

Weather and Climate Lesson Assessment Answer Key

Read each question carefully and then answer on the lines provided.

10 pts.

1. Explain the difference between weather and climate.

   Weather is the day-to-day condition of an area, but climate is the long-term pattern of weather over time.

9 pts.

2. Describe the three major climate types: polar, temperate, and tropical.

   Polar climates are cold and have long, dark winters and short summers. Tropical climates are very warm and can be very moist, which allows for many plants to grow. Temperate climates have temperatures between tropical and polar climates and have distinct seasons and changing weather. Most of the United States is in a temperate climate zone.

5 pts.

3. How does average temperature change as latitude decreases from the poles to the equator? Why?

   Temperatures are warmer closer to the equator because the sun's energy is more direct there.

Study the map on page 3.

5 pts.

4. Name a city that most likely has a tropical climate.

   Accept Jakarta or Kuala Lumpur.

224

Name _____ Date _____

5 pts.

5. Name a city that most likely has a temperate climate.

Accept Shanghai, Addis Ababa, or Buenos Aires.

5 pts.

6. Name a city that most likely has a polar climate.

Accept Banff, Helsinki, or Minsk.

Name   Date

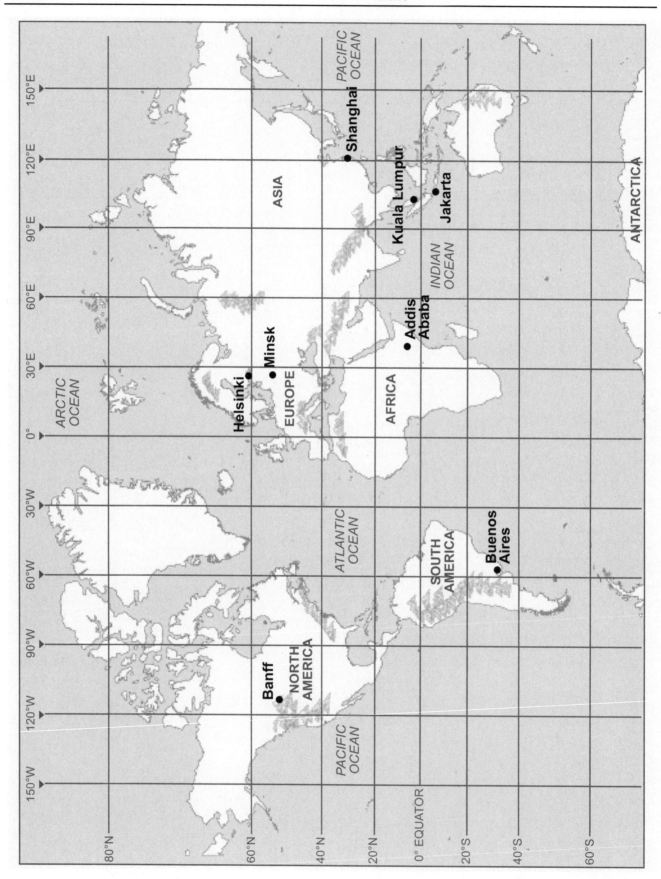

Learning Coach Guide
Lesson 12: Factors Affecting Climate

Lesson Objectives

- Analyze how the following factors affect climate: land elevation, geographic location, ocean currents, and proximity to bodies of water.
- Explain how mountain ranges and other major geographical features influence climate patterns.
- Recognize the major influences of solar energy on wind, ocean currents, and the water cycle.

PREPARE

Approximate lesson time is 60 minutes.

Materials

For the Student

    📠 Home Sweet Biome

    📠 North America Map

    markers or crayons

For the Adult

    📠 Home Sweet Biome Answer Key

Keywords and Pronunciation

conduction : the transfer of heat between two adjoining objects, caused by a temperature difference between the objects

convection (kuhn-VEK-shuhn) : the transfer of heat by the circulation or movement of the heated parts of a liquid or gas

radiation : the process in which energy is emitted by one body, transmitted through an intervening medium or space, and absorbed by another body

TEACH
Activity 1: Factors Affecting Climate (Online)
Instructions

Your student will explore factors that affect climate. After reading the activity, your student can read about the different climate zones in the United States at http://www.srh.noaa.gov/jetstream/global/climate.htm. Your student will use this information to try the climate quiz below. Each question in the quiz puts the student in a climate region during January or August. Read each description to your student. Have your student decide if the description represents the normal climate for that location or if it is abnormal.

Climate Quiz

1) You are in Denver, Colorado on January 22nd for a ski trip. It is 25 degrees Fahrenheit and snowing heavily.

2) You're at Disney World in Orlando, Florida on August 25th. It's 65 degrees Fahrenheit with light rain.

3) You're visiting Las Vegas, Nevada on August 2nd. The weather is warm and it has been raining lightly for two days.

4) You're at the Empire State Building in New York on January 15th. It is 70 degrees Fahrenheit and sunny.

5) You are in Seattle, Washington on January 27th. It is rainy and 47 degrees Fahrenheit.

Answers:

1) Normal

2) Abnormal

3) Abnormal

4) Abnormal

5) Normal

Activity 2: Home Sweet Biome (Offline)

Instructions

Your student will be investigating the biomes that make up North America. He may need access to a library to conduct his research. He may also use the Internet to complete this activity.

Activity 3: Home Sweet Biome (Online)

ASSESS

Lesson Assessment: Factors Affecting Climate (Online)

Students will complete an online assessment based on the lesson objectives. The assessment will be scored by the computer. The attached answer key is the most current and may not coincide with previously printed guides.

Name _____   Date _____

Home Sweet Biome Answer Key

Step 2: Researching Biomes

Now that your interest inventory is complete, you can start to research different areas to find a place that meets your wants and needs. North America can be divided into seven areas separated by the climate and plant and animal life in them. These seven areas are called biomes.

Using multimedia resources, you will research six biomes (unless you plan to live underwater in the seventh biome, the ocean) and complete the data chart and answer the questions below. The websites below are a good starting point but you may also use books or the Grolier's Online Encyclopedia found in Unit Resources.

Refer to the lesson for links to each website.

* Biome Basics
* World Biomes
* What's it Like Where You Live?

BIOME	CLIMATE	TERRAIN or LAND PATTERN	WEATHER PATTERNS
Tundra	Very cold and dry all year	Mountainous, only sparse vegetation in summer, soil is frozen most of the year	Fierce winds, very low temperatures, very low precipitation, snow and ice
Grasslands	Very hot in the summer, very cold in the winter	Flat, grassy, mostly low vegetation	Very dry summers, extremes in temperature, moderate precipitation, tornadoes and storms
Desert	Hot and dry all year. Hot days, cold nights	Mountainous, sandy, rocky with little vegetation	Very dry, high temperatures, extremely low precipitation and humidity, but flash floods possible
Taiga	Warm, rainy summers. Very cold winters. Long nights in winter, long days in summer	Mountainous, dense coniferous vegetation	Rain in summer, low snow in winters, moderate precipitation
Rain forest	Tropical: High heat and humidity all year Temperate: Cool temperatures, high humidity	Mountainous, extremely dense vegetation	Tropical: high precipitation, temperature, and humidity Temperate: high precipitation, low temperatures
Temperate forest	Four distinct seasons	Low mountains or hills, dense vegetation, trees	Average temperature 50 degrees Fahrenheit, warm/hot in summer, cold in winter, high precipitation and humidity

Name _____   Date _____

1. Which resource provided you with the most information? Write the title and provide the link if it is a website.

    Check to see that your student has provided the title and hyperlink, if applicable to his

    preferred resource.

2. Define the term *biome.*

    A biome is a large geographical area described by the dominant plant and animal life, climate,

    and weather patterns. Terrestrial biomes include: tropical rain forest, temperate rain forest,

    taiga, grasslands, deserts, and temperate deciduous forests.

3. What effect does the terrain of a biome have on its climate and weather?

    Biomes located near coasts will tend to be cooler than those located inland such as

    grasslands. Mountainous biomes may be cooler and less windy.

4. On the map of North America, use colored pencils or crayons to color the boundaries of each biome. Make a key.

    Check your student's map. Desert biomes are found in the southwestern United States.

    Grassland biomes are found in the Midwest, starting in southern Canada and ending in

    southeastern Mexico. Rainforest biomes can be found in southern Mexico, southern Florida,

    and the Caribbean. Taigas are found throughout most of the top half of Canada, except for

    the northernmost regions, which are tundra biomes. Temperate forests are found in the

    southeastern United States.

Step 3 and 4: Where do you want to live?

You will need the answers to the interest inventory and your biome research to complete this section.

5. Which biome contains the climate you prefer?

    _____

6. Why did you choose this biome?

    _____

    _____

    _____

Name ______________________ Date ______________________

7. How would your life be different in this biome?

____

____

Step 5: Tell the folks back home

8. Tell your family and friends back home about your new home! Draw a picture of your biome. Write a postcard-sized note about why you love your new home!

STAMP

Learning Coach Guide
Lesson 13: Lab: Global Warming

To prepare for this lesson on the greenhouse effect, your student will first explore the online lesson. The lesson describes how the sun's energy is converted to heat energy and how energy can be radiated to the surface of the earth by the atmosphere. Information is given about global warming, and the role of human activities that may be contributing to changes in the environment.

Your student will then visit websites created by the United States Environmental Protection Agency, and PBS on the topic of greenhouse gases and global warming. Using this information, your student will create a concept map. The concept map provides your student with an opportunity to summarize the information gathered in a fun and exciting way and will help foster a better understanding about the relationship between human actions and global warming.

Lesson Objectives

- Explain how the greenhouse effect and the amount of carbon dioxide in the atmosphere are thought to be connected to global warming.
- Describe two possible results of global warming.
- Define global warming as an increase in the average atmospheric temperature.

PREPARE

Approximate lesson time is 60 minutes.

Materials

For the Student

 📖 Understanding Global Warming

 Science Notebook

 paper

 pencil, colored

Optional

 glue or tape

 newspaper - or magazines

 scissors

For the Adult

 📖 Understanding Global Warming Answer Key

Keywords and Pronunciation

global warming : an increase in the average temperature of the atmosphere surrounding the earth that is capable of causing a change in climate

greenhouse effect : the process in which the absorption of short wave radiation by the atmosphere heats up a planet

greenhouse gases : atmospheric gases that contribute to the greenhouse effect that include water vapor, nitrous oxide, methane, and carbon dioxide, which is the most abundant

---

TEACH
Activity 1: LAB: Global Warming (Online)

Instructions

Your student will view data and read information about the possible relationship between human actions and global warming.

Activity 2: Understanding Greenhouse Gases and Global Warming (Offline)

Instructions

Your student has learned about a possible relationship between human activity and an increase in global temperature. The scientific community neither has a unanimous conclusion about the nature of the relationship, nor on the likely implications. Your student will read excerpts of scientific data about this issue. Then, considering all of the information, your student will create a concept map to help understand the various ideas involved with global warming.

To prepare for this lesson on the greenhouse effect, your student will first review the online lesson about how the sun's energy is converted to heat energy and how energy can be radiated to the surface of the earth by the atmosphere as well as directly by the sun. Your student will view data online by visiting some websites and create a concept map. The concept map provides your student with an opportunity to summarize the information discovered in a fun and exciting way to help understand the relationship between human actions and global warming.

ASSESS
Lesson Assessment: Lab: Global Warming (Online)

Review your student's responses on the Understanding Global Warming lab and input the results online. The attached answer key is the most current and may not coincide with previously printed guides.

Name _____   Date _____

Understanding Global Warming Answer Key

Materials

Science Notebook
paper
colored pencils
scissors
tape
glue

Purpose

The scientific community has been tracking the changes in climate and weather patterns for many years now. Your student has learned that there may be a possible link between human activity and an increase in global temperature and this could result in some unpleasant effects on the earth's atmosphere. The greenhouse effect has a helpful effect on our atmosphere that contributes to life on earth. In this lab, your student will visit some websites to investigate more about what the scientists are learning. Your student will create a concept map to help summarize the ideas presented in this lesson.

Review of the Concept Map

A sample concept map and word bank is provided to help you evaluate your student's work. However, your student's diagram may look quite different from the one provided. In this laboratory, your student should try to be creative and think of as many ways as possible to show the relationships among the ideas presented.

Word Bank

burning fossil fuels	deforestation	car exhaust
solar energy	decaying organic material	cement production
end of Ice Age	helps plants grow	human exhalation
burning coal	keeps earth warm	polar ice caps melting
oceans rising		

Procedure

Visit the websites listed below and review the information provided. While you are reading over the information, search for the words listed in the word bank.

EPA, Climate Change - Greenhouse Gas Emissions: http://www.epa.gov/climatechange/emissions/index.html

EPA Kids Site, Greenhouse Effect: http://epa.gov/climatechange/kids/basics/today/greenhouse-effect.html

Nova Online, Greenhouse - Green Planet: http://www.pbs.org/wgbh/nova/ice/greenhouse.html

What Triggers Ice Ages?

http://www.pbs.org/wgbh/nova/earth/cause-ice-age.html

Steps

1. List under the box Man-Made Sources some examples of how CO_2 may be produced by human activities; one answer could be car emissions. After you have finished the first step, expand your map by adding boxes to show the possible ways that the earth's atmosphere could be hurt by global warming.

2. List under the box Natural Sources some ways that CO_2 is produced naturally; one example might be volcanic activity. When you have finished the first step, expand your map by adding boxes to show the possible ways in which greenhouse gases help the earth's atmosphere.

3. Relax and visualize the information in your head. To make this concept map more exciting, you can cut out pictures from newspapers or magazines showing examples of how CO_2 is made. Or you may want to draw examples of the things you are discovering.

4. Gather paper, markers, and a ruler and some shapes to trace (optional).

5. You should try sketching the diagram in pencil first.

6. You might need to draw more than one map, or think of ways to connect smaller maps to show all of the information. Be creative!

7. Use colors or shapes to show differences between main ideas and supporting details.

8. Check to see that your map is clear and makes sense to you. If not, revise it!

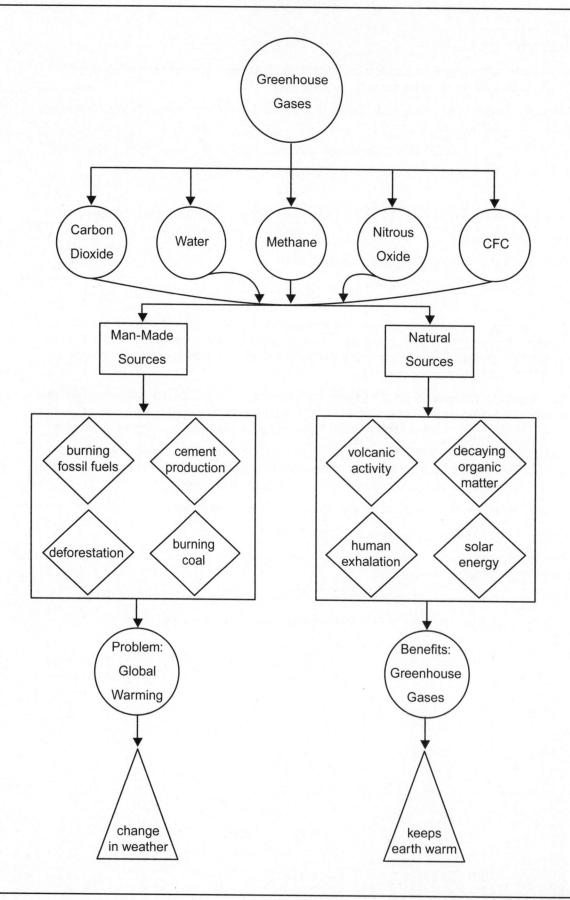

Use the concept map you prepared to help you answer the following questions.

1. Describe at least two things that we can do today to help protect the earth and reduce levels of CO_2.

    Some examples might be recycling cans and bottles, reducing the use of CO_2 by choosing to share a ride to work or school, planting trees to help the environment.

2. Briefly explain how greenhouse gases, carbon dioxide in particular, can absorb and radiate heat inside the earth's atmosphere thereby contributing to the greenhouse effect.

    Much of the solar energy that travels to earth is absorbed by the earth's surface. The earth converts this energy into heat, which is released into the atmosphere. The greenhouse gases absorb the heat and send it back to the earth's surface. This process is called the greenhouse effect. If there is an increase in greenhouse gases in the atmosphere, too much of the heat may be trapped causing an abnormal increase in the earth's average surface temperature.

3. Read What Triggers Ice Ages?. Briefly describe what you think the world would be like if the amount of greenhouse gases in the atmosphere were reduced to levels like those during the Ice Age.

    If there were less greenhouse gases, much of the infrared radiation that is converted to heat today would not be trapped in the earth's atmosphere. The earth's temperature would cool, and a new Ice Age would occur. Many plants and animals could not survive in this new condition, oceans would freeze, and weather patterns would change.

Name _____ Date _____

LAB: Global Warming Lesson Assessment Answer Key

Answers:

1. Some examples might be recycling cans and bottles, reducing the use of CO_2 by choosing to share a ride to work or school, planting trees to help the environment.

2. Much of the solar energy that travels to earth is absorbed by the earth's surface. The earth converts this energy into heat, which is released into the atmosphere. The greenhouse gases absorb the heat and send it back to the earth's surface. This process is called the greenhouse effect. If there is an increase in greenhouse gases in the atmosphere, too much of the heat may be trapped causing an abnormal increase in the earth's average surface temperature.

3. If there were less greenhouse gases, much of the infrared radiation that is converted to heat today would not be trapped in the earth's atmosphere. The earth's temperature would cool, and a new Ice Age would occur. Many plants and animals could not survive in this new condition, oceans would freeze, and weather patterns would change.

Learning Coach Guide
Lesson 14: Unit Review

Before taking the Unit Assessment, your student will review what he has learned about air, weather, and climate.

Lesson Objectives

- Name and describe the properties of the four main types of air masses that influence weather in North America, locate them on a map, and describe their typical influence on weather.
- Compare the properties of low- and high-pressure areas in terms of air density, pressure, humidity, air motion, and types of associated weather.
- Describe the three mechanisms of heat energy transfer to and among the land, ocean, and air.
- Explain how uneven heating of the earth and the Coriolis effect result in the earth's prevailing winds.
- Explain how large lakes, mountains, and surface ocean currents such as the Gulf Stream can influence climate.
- Explain the main energy transfers in the earth system, explain the greenhouse effect, and recognize that relative constancy of the earth's climates requires that the amount of energy received from the sun roughly equals the amount reflected and radiated from earth into space.
- Name and locate on a world map the three main climate zones (polar, temperate, and tropical) and explain variation in climate in terms of intensity of solar energy, wind, landforms, and ocean currents.
- Describe how air masses interact at cold, warm, stationary, and occluded fronts and describe the clouds and weather they may produce.

PREPARE

Approximate lesson time is 60 minutes.

Materials

For the Student

    💻 Weather and Climate Review

For the Adult

    💻 Weather and Climate Review Answer Key

TEACH
Activity 1: Air, Weather, and Climate *(Online)*

Instructions

In this unit, your student has learned a lot of information about the earth's climates, weather, and biospheres. In this lesson, your student will review some of the material explored in this unit. This will help your student prepare for the Unit Assessment.

Activity 2: Weather and Climate Unit Review (Online)
Instructions
Looking back, your student has learned a lot of information about the atmosphere, climate, weather, and the biosphere. Does your student remember the difference between weather and climate? Your student will discover how much information he can remember about the concepts presented in the unit by working through this review.

Name _____   Date _____

Review Answer Key

Directions

Read each question carefully and place your answers in the spaces provided. Have the teacher review your work. When you are finished, place your review in your Science Notebook.

1. Explain the atmospheric process that creates the greenhouse effect.
   Certain gases in the atmosphere absorb energy that would otherwise be lost in space. This
   increased energy in the atmosphere causes warmer surface temperatures on the earth.

   _____

2. Explain why air moves from areas of high pressure to areas of low pressure.
   Heating or cooling of air creates differences in air pressure. Cool air (which is denser)
   generally has higher pressure than warm air. As air accumulates above the earth's surface, air
   pressure will rise. This air will gradually move toward a region of lower pressure. The change
   in air pressure between two air masses is called the air pressure gradient.

3. Think about how climate and weather relate to the four spheres of the earth's system. An example would be that land and water heat and cool at different rates, creating coastal winds.
   This question is open-ended and doesn't need to be graded. It encourages students to think
   about what they have learned in this unit.

   _____

4. Write down some of your own examples of how the spheres relate to climate and weather.
   This question is open-ended and doesn't need to be graded. It encourages students to think
   about what they have learned in this unit.

   _____

5. Complete the table by deciding which climate type is correct for the region. Some answers are already given in the table.

Air Mass	Temperature (Is it Warm or Cold?)	Humidity (Is it Humid or Dry?)	Air Pressure (Is it High or Low?)
Maritime Polar	**Cold**	Humid	Low
Maritime Tropical	Warm	Humid	Low
Continental Polar	Cold	**Dry**	High
Continental Tropical	Warm	Dry	**High**
Arctic	Cold	Dry	High

Learning Coach Guide
Lesson 15: Unit Assessment

Lesson Objectives

- Name and describe the properties of the four main types of air masses that influence weather in North America, locate them on a map, and describe their typical influence on weather.
- Compare the properties of low- and high-pressure areas in terms of air density, pressure, humidity, air motion, and types of associated weather.
- Describe the three mechanisms of heat energy transfer to and among the land, ocean, and air.
- Explain how uneven heating of the earth and the Coriolis effect result in the earth's prevailing winds.
- Explain how large lakes, mountains, and surface ocean currents such as the Gulf Stream can influence climate.
- Explain the main energy transfers in the earth system, explain the greenhouse effect, and recognize that relative constancy of the earth's climates requires that the amount of energy received from the sun roughly equals the amount reflected and radiated from earth into space.
- Name and locate on a world map the three main climate zones (polar, temperate, and tropical) and explain variation in climate in terms of intensity of solar energy, wind, landforms, and ocean currents.
- Describe how air masses interact at cold, warm, stationary, and occluded fronts and describe the clouds and weather they may produce.

PREPARE

Approximate lesson time is 60 minutes.

ASSESS

Unit Assessment: Air, Weather, and Climate, Part 1 (*Online*)

Students will complete an online assessment of the objectives covered so far in this unit. The assessment will be scored by the computer. The attached answer key is the most current and may not coincide with previously printed guides.

Unit Assessment: Air, Weather, and Climate, Part 2 (*Offline*)

Students will complete an offline Unit Assessment. Print the assessment and have students complete it on their own. Use the answer key to score the assessment, and then enter the results online. The attached answer key is the most current and may not coincide with previously printed guides.

Learning Coach Guide
Lesson 1: Semester 1 Review

To prepare for the Semester 1 Assessment, have your student complete the Semester 1 Review. Your student will review the material presented in this semester by revisiting key concepts, illustrations, and animations.

Looking back, your student has learned a lot of information this semester. Does your student recall how the ocean surface currents are caused by the winds or the difference between weather and climate? This review lesson will help your student remember some of the main concepts presented this past semester.

Lesson Objectives

- Explain how sedimentary rocks are formed and identify features that help determine the type of environment in which they formed.
- State the defining characteristics of a mineral.
- Explain how properties of minerals can be used in their identification.
- Explain how metamorphic rocks are formed.
- Describe evidence that supported the theory of continental drift.
- Describe key features of the theory of plate tectonics.
- Recognize and explain methods by which scientists determine the sequence of geological events, life forms present, and environmental conditions in the past geological eras.
- Describe how air masses interact at cold, warm, stationary, and occluded fronts and describe the clouds and weather they may produce.
- Compare the properties of low- and high-pressure areas in terms of air density, pressure, humidity, air motion, and types of associated weather.
- Describe features on maps such as coordinate systems, scales, directional indicators, keys, symbols, and contour lines.
- Describe major agents of mechanical weathering and of chemical weathering, how the agents cause each kind of weathering, and how mechanical weathering and chemical weathering interact to enhance each other's effects.
- Name and locate on a world map the three main climate zones (polar, temperate, and tropical) and explain variation in climate in terms of intensity of solar energy, wind, landforms, and ocean currents.
- Describe the basic components of the earth's physical systems: atmosphere, biosphere, lithosphere, hydrosphere, and magnetosphere.
- Explain latitude and longitude and recognize them as providing a primary coordinate system for reference to places on the earth.
- Describe major types of soil in terms of porosity, permeability, and climates in which they are found.
- Explain how igneous rocks form and recognize how physical properties of an igneous rock reveal its origin.
- Recognize the principle of uniformitarianism and its importance in determining historical events based on geological information.
- Describe the geologic time scale and provide examples of major geological and biological events of each era.

- Recognize that movements in the earth's crust create seismic waves, which scientists study to learn about earth's interior.
- Explain how uneven heating of the earth and the Coriolis effect create the earth's prevailing winds.
- Explain the main energy transfers of the earth's energy budget, explain the greenhouse effect, and recognize that relative constancy of the earth's climates requires that the amount of energy received from the sun equals the amount reflected and radiated from earth into space.

PREPARE

Approximate lesson time is 60 minutes.

Materials

For the Student

📖 Semester 1 Review

For the Adult

📖 Semester 1 Review Answer Key

TEACH

Activity 1: Semester 1 Review (Online)

Instructions

Your student will prepare for the Semester 1 Assessment. The Semester 1 Review has two parts. After your student has completed the online portion, have him print the Semester 1 Review. Use the answer key to score your student's work.

Activity 2: Semester 1 Review (Online)

Instructions

Now that your student has completed the online portion, print the Semester 1 Review and use the answer key to score your student's work. Your student may place the completed review in the Science Notebook.

Name _____   Date _____

Semester 1 Review Answer Key

Introduction

Looking back, do you recall how the ocean surface currents are caused by the winds? Do you remember the difference between weather and climate? Could you describe the different layers and characteristics of the biosphere? It's time to discover how much information you remember about the material you have learned this semester. Work through this review. Read the questions carefully and place your answers in the spaces provided. Have your teacher review your work when you are finished.

The Spheres of Earth

Imagine the earth as a series of spheres, like the layers of an onion.

1. If you observed the earth from space, which sphere would you see first?

   atmosphere

2. Which sphere includes the rocks and minerals?

   lithosphere

Maps

3. Describe the difference between lines of longitude and lines of latitude. Explain why they are useful.

   Longitude lines run from the North Pole to the South Pole. Latitude lines are parallel with the

   equator, stretching from east to west. These lines of latitude and longitude are useful because

   they help us locate places on a map. Specific points can be identified with the coordinates of

   longitude and latitude.

Maps and Legends

Some smaller maps, such as road maps, have symbols that indicate places of interest. These could be schools, campsites, airports, or a variety of other things. A key, or map legend, tells you what each symbol means. Scales can help you figure out the distance between two places, and a compass rose indicates the four main directions: north, south, east, and west.

4. In the box on page 2, draw a map of a town. Use your imagination. Include at least three different places of interest, a map legend, a scale, and a compass rose. Don't forget to name your town. Use your map to answer questions 5 and 6.

5. To show the elevation of different areas, what does your town map need?

   Contour lines show areas of the same elevation.

6. Choose a place of interest on your map and imagine that it is located at the highest point in your town. Draw contour lines on your map to show that this area has the highest elevation.

Making Soil

Soil is the product of weathering. Soil gives plants a place to root as well as the water and nutrients they need to survive. Two factors influence the amount of water in a soil: porosity and permeability. Define each term in the spaces provided.

7. Porosity

    Porosity refers to the amount of water that a soil can hold, based on the spaces available within the soil. Porosity is actually the ratio of the volume of pores in a soil to the total volume.

8. Permeability

    Permeability is the ability of a soil to allow water or fluid to pass through it. Permeability relates to the speed at which water flows through a soil.

9. Soil can be divided into three categories: sand, silt, and clay. Complete the chart below that describes the porosity and permeability of each soil. Choose High, Moderate, or Low.

Characteristics	Sand	Silt	Clay
Porosity	Low	Moderate	High
Permeability	High	Moderate	Low

Rocks

Minerals are not the only substances that are separated into groups. Rocks are classified, too. They are organized into three groups based on how they form: igneous, sedimentary, and metamorphic. Do you remember how each type of rock forms?

10. Igneous

These rocks form when molten lava or magma solidifies.

11. Sedimentary

These rocks form when sediments are compressed over a long period of time or when chemicals precipitate out of water.

12. Metamorphic

These rocks form when extreme heat and pressure cause rocks to change.

13. Igneous rocks are classified into two different types: extrusive and intrusive. Explain the difference between extrusive and intrusive igneous rocks.

Intrusive rocks form below the earth's surface. Extrusive rocks form on the earth's surface.

14. Explain how scientists determine age with using relative dating and absolute dating methods.

Relative dating compares two or more objects to determine which one is older. For relative dating, a scientist would observe the sequence of layers of rock, using relative position to determine which one is older. Younger rock is near the top and older rock is near the bottom. Absolute dating determines the actual age of objects. For absolute dating, a scientist would apply radiometric dating techniques to determine the exact age of a mineral grain.

Continental Drift and Plate Tectonics

A map of the earth drawn 200 million years ago would look much different from the world maps we draw today.

15. How did Wegener describe the world that existed 200 million years ago?

Wegener believed that the continents were once connected as one supercontinent called
Pangaea. A map showing the earth 200 million years ago when the continents were merged
into one large landmass, would look very different from a map that shows the world as it
is today.

16. Describe specific findings on earth's seafloor that supported the theory of plate tectonics.

Scientists discovered a volcanic rift in the middle of the Atlantic Ocean. At the mid-ocean
ridge, scientists found that the ocean floor is magnetized normally and aligned with earth's
current magnetic field. Also, they found that some parts of the seafloor demonstrate reverse
magnetization. Distinct patterns of magnetization appear in symmetrical "stripes" on each side
of the mid-ocean ridge. The age of rocks that make up the seafloor is directly related to their
distance from this ridge. This shows that the seafloor has spread outward from the mid-ocean
ridge over time.

17. Describe how scientists use seismic data to analyze the earth's interior structure.

Scientists studied the movement of seismic waves during earthquakes. They collected
evidence about S-waves, which do not travel through liquids. Data showed that these S-waves
do not travel through earth's outer core. Using this information, geologists determined that the
outer core is made of molten rock, and the inner core is made of solid rock.

18. Wind is an important aspect of weather. The rotation of the earth causes the Coriolis effect. Explain this phenomenon.

The Coriolis effect refers to the deflection or curved pattern of the prevailing winds that blow
across the surface of the earth; these winds do not move in a straight-line pattern. Winds
in the northern hemisphere rotate counterclockwise, and winds in the southern hemisphere
rotate clockwise.

Climate

Climate refers to the weather patterns that characterize a particular region over a long period of time.

19. How does latitude influence climate?

Climates at lower latitudes are usually warmer. Climates at higher latitudes and near the poles
are generally colder.

20. Describe the three climate zones. Name a country or a place located in each climate zone.

The polar climate zone is extremely cold and icy. The North and South Pole are included in the

polar climate zone. A temperate zone has variable weather and experiences a regular change

of seasons. Most of the United States is in the temperate zone. The tropical climate zone

is characterized by hot and humid weather. A large part of Mexico is located in the tropical

climate zone.

21. Describe how and why each of these variables affects climate.

Ocean currents:

Ocean currents bring warm or cold water into an area. The water heats or cools the air above

it, which causes warmer or cooler temperatures on nearby land.

Ocean winds:

Air masses that form above the ocean tend to be humid. Ocean winds can carry this moist air

over land, where fog may form and rain may fall.

Mountains:

Mountains are colder than other land areas located at the same latitude. When an air mass

moves over a mountain range, the air may lose much of its moisture, creating a wet climate

on the windward side and a dry climate on the leeward side.

Energy Budget

Overall, the earth's climates are relatively stable.

22. Why are earth's climates so stable?

To maintain climatic stability, the energy received from the sun must roughly equal the

amount of energy radiated back into space. Otherwise, the earth would tend to heat up or

cool down.

23. Carbon dioxide, methane, water vapor, and other gases in the atmosphere absorb light energy, heat up, and radiate this energy toward the surface of the earth. What process does this describe?

the greenhouse effect

24. The greenhouse effect isn't always bad for the earth. When does the greenhouse effect become problematic?

The greenhouse effect keeps earth warmer than it would be otherwise by keeping heat from escaping into space. The greenhouse effect becomes a problem when excess carbon dioxide and other greenhouse gases in the atmosphere trap too much heat, leading to temperature increases on earth's surface.

Learning Coach Guide
Lesson 2: Semester 1 Assessment

In this lesson, your student will take an assessment that has two parts. The student will first complete the online portion. The second part is a printed assessment. Use the answer key to score your student's work on the printed assessment, and then enter the results online.

Lesson Objectives

- State the defining characteristics of a mineral.
- Describe evidence that supported the theory of continental drift.
- Describe key features of the theory of plate tectonics.
- Recognize and explain methods by which scientists determine the sequence of geological events, life forms present, and environmental conditions in the past geological eras.
- Compare the properties of low- and high-pressure areas in terms of air density, pressure, humidity, air motion, and types of associated weather.
- Describe features on maps such as coordinate systems, scales, directional indicators, keys, symbols, and contour lines.
- Describe major types of soil in terms of porosity, permeability, and climates in which they are found.
- Describe the geologic time scale and provide examples of major geological and biological events of each era.
- Name and locate on a world map the three main climate zones (polar, temperate, and tropical) and explain variation in climate in terms of intensity of solar energy, wind, landforms, and ocean currents.
- Describe how air masses interact at cold, warm, stationary, and occluded fronts and describe the clouds and weather they may produce.
- Explain latitude and longitude and recognize them as providing a primary coordinate system for reference to places on the earth.
- Explain how uneven heating of the earth and the Coriolis effect create the earth's prevailing winds.
- Explain how metamorphic rocks are formed.
- Explain how sedimentary rocks are formed and identify features that help determine the type of environment in which they formed.
- Describe major agents of mechanical weathering and of chemical weathering, how the agents cause each kind of weathering, and how mechanical weathering and chemical weathering interact to enhance each other's effects.
- Explain how properties of minerals can be used in their identification.
- Describe evidence that supported the theory of continental drift.
- Describe key features of the theory of plate tectonics.
- Explain the main energy transfers in the earth system, explain the greenhouse effect, and recognize that relative constancy of the earth's climates requires that the amount of energy received from the sun roughly equals the amount reflected and radiated from earth into space.
- Describe the basic components of the earth's physical systems: atmosphere, biosphere, lithosphere, hydrosphere, and magnetosphere.

- Explain how igneous rocks form and recognize how physical properties of an igneous rock reveal its origin.
- Recognize the principle of uniformitarianism and its importance in determining historical events based on geological information.

PREPARE

Approximate lesson time is 60 minutes.

ASSESS

Semester Assessment: Semester 1 Assessment, Part 1 (*Online*)

Students will complete an assessment based on the semester objectives. This part of the assessment is online and will be scored by the computer. The attached answer key is the most current and may not coincide with previously printed guides.

Semester Assessment: Semester 1 Assessment, Part 2 (*Offline*)

Students will complete an offline Semester assessment. Print the assessment and have students complete it on their own. Use the answer key to score the assessment, and then enter the results online. The attached answer key is the most current and may not coincide with previously printed guides.